SCHOLASTIC
ART & WRITING AWARDS
PRESENTS

THE
BEST
TEEN
WRITING
OF
2015

Edited by
MICHAELA COPLEN
2013 National Student Poet
2014 Silver Medal with
Distinction Portfolio Recipient

Scholastic
Art & Writing
Awards

D0050162

For information or permission, contact:
Alliance for Young Artists & Writers
557 Broadway
New York, NY 10012
www.artandwriting.org

No part of this publication may be reproduced in whole or
in part, or stored in a retrieval system, or transmitted in
any form or by any means, including electronic, mechanical,
photocopying, microfilming, recording or otherwise, without
written permission from the publisher.

Editor: Michaela Coplen
Director, Programs: Scott Larner
Managing Editor: Hannah Jones
Art Director: Meg Callery
Copy Editor: Ingrid Accardi
Production Assistant: Sazia Afrin
Cover art: *Untitled* (diptych), Photograph by Sammie Concilio,
Grade 12, Age 17, Brooklyn, NY.

© 2015 Alliance for Young Artists & Writers
All rights reserved. Printed in the United States of America
Anthology printing, August 2015
ISBN13: 978-0-545-94260-7
ISBN10: 0-545-94260-8

DEDICATION

The Best Teen Writing of 2015 is dedicated to the inaugural Scholastic Art & Writing Awards Alumni Council. The Alumni Council consists of artists, writers, professionals, and individuals who are all deeply connected to the arts.

The 2015 Alumni Council members are:
Tammy Cassie Chan, '10
Winston Chieminlinski, '06
Haris A. Durrani, '11
Tasha Garcia, '07
Katiuscia Gregoire, '13
Molly Hensley-Clancy, '08
Zara Kessler, '08
Timothy Hyunsoo Lee, '06
Justin Nissley, '01
Iviva Olenick, '93
Antonio Pulgarin, '07
Mara Sprafkin, '98

The Scholastic Art & Writing Awards Alumni Council champions the arts and advocates for teenagers in diverse communities across the nation while encouraging other alumni to remain connected to the Awards program for unique networking opportunities. The Scholastic Art & Writing Awards Alumni Council advises the Alliance for Young Artists & Writers' staff leadership on alumni residencies, outreach, and workshops, as well as audience development.

Visit **www.artandwriting.org/alumnicouncil** to learn more about the Alumni Council, and stay connected on LinkedIn.

TABLE OF CONTENTS

Poetry

ABOUT THE BEST TEEN WRITING OF 2015

The pieces featured in *The Best Teen Writing of 2015* were selected from work that earned National Medals in the 2015 Scholastic Art & Writing Awards. The Scholastic Awards, a national program presented by the Alliance for Young Artists & Writers, identifies and showcases teenagers with exceptional artistic and literary talent. Founded in 1923, the program celebrates the accomplishments of creative students and extends opportunities for recognition, exhibition, publication, and scholarships.

This year, 579 students earned National Medals in writing categories. The works selected for this publication represent the diversity of the National Medalists, including age and grade, gender, genre, geography, and subject matter. They also present a spectrum of the insight and creative intellect that inform many of the pieces.

A complete listing of National Medalists and online galleries of awarded works of art and writing can be found on our website at **www.artandwriting.org**. Visit our site to see how to enter the 2016 Scholastic Art & Writing Awards, as well as a list of our scholarship partners and ways you can partner with the Alliance to support young artists and writers in your community.

Some of the writing selections have been excerpted. Go to **www.artandwriting.org/galleries** to read all of the work as it was submitted.

ABOUT THE SCHOLASTIC ART & WRITING AWARDS

For more than 90 years, the Scholastic Art & Writing Awards have recognized the exceptional vision of our nation's youth. Established in 1923 by Scholastic founder Maurice R. Robinson, the Scholastic Awards have grown to become the nation's highest honor and largest source of scholarships for creative teens. Through a nationwide partner network of 118 Affiliates, the 2015 Awards received more than 300,000 submissions— 20% more than the previous year—spanning 28 categories of art and writing. Students are encouraged by their educators, both in schools and through out-of-school programs, to submit their original work. All students in grades 7 through 12, whether in public, private, or home schools, can apply. Notable Scholastic Awards alumni include Andy Warhol, Sylvia Plath, Cy Twombly, John Baldessari, Kay WalkingStick, Richard Avedon, Stephen King, Luis Jiménez, and Truman Capote—to name just a few.

RECOGNITION In 2015, the Alliance and our Affiliate partners provided recognition at the regional and national levels to more than 60,000 teens. Of these top regional award recipients, more than 17,000 went on for consideration at the national level, with more than 2,000 students receiving National Medals. National Medalists in the poetry category also have the opportunity to be selected for the National Student Poets Program (**www.artandwriting.org/nspp**).

EXHIBITION More than 1,000 works of art and writing by National Medalists were shown in the Art.Write.Now.2015 National Exhibition at the Sheila C. Johnson Design Center at Parsons School for Design at The New School and Pratt

Institute's Pratt Manhattan Gallery. Throughout the year, selections of work will travel the country with the Art.Write. Now.Tour 2015—with upcoming stops in Springs Preserve, NV; Grand Rapids, MI; and Bozeman, MT—or spend a full year on display at the U.S. Department of Education or the President's Committee on the Arts and the Humanities in Washington, D.C.

PUBLICATION The Alliance features works by National Medalists of both art and writing in our annual National Catalog. Additionally, we publish a collection of exemplary written works in this anthology, *The Best Teen Writing*, and a chapbook that features works from the National Student Poets. These publications are distributed free of charge to schools, students, educators, museums, libraries, and arts organizations across the country. Our searchable online gallery of more than 30,000 art and literary works from 2010 onward can be accessed at **www.artandwriting.org/galleries**.

SCHOLARSHIPS The Alliance distributes more than $250,000 in direct scholarships annually to National Medalists. Students can leverage success in the Awards through our Scholarship Partners, a national network of dozens of esteemed universities, colleges, and art schools for additional opportunities. Additionally, our Alliance Summer Arts Program pairs students with top-tier summer arts and writing intensives around the nation, providing scholarships to talented emerging artists and writers.

2015 SCHOLASTIC ART & WRITING AWARDS
NATIONAL WRITING JURORS

American Voices
Celia Bell
Jared Dummit
Alexandra Franklin
Christina Gonzalez
Kevin Hong
Nicole Levy
Loretta López
Rachel Rothenberg
Diane Ward

Best-in-Grade
Kwame Alexander
Rita Feinstein
Luke Hodges
Pauline Holdsworth
Lynne Rae Perkins
Kerri Schlottman

Creativity & Citizenship
Beth Ain
Michael Keller
Ron Russell

Critical Essay
Haris Durrani
Alfred L. Schreiber
Linda Vasu

Dramatic Script
Juliana Francis-Kelly

Mitch Mattson
Linda McFall

Flash Fiction
Phyllis Hunter
Amy Lawless
Stephen Sherrill

Gedenk Award for Tolerance
Paula Freedman
Ann Oster
Natalie Standiford

Humor
Katherine Erskine
David Krasnow
Eric Levai

Journalism
Ralph Gardner
Jyothi Natarajan
Mohana Ravindranath

Personal Essay / Memoir
Chris Bannon
Rebecca Bondor
Kathryn Cullen-DuPont
Melissa Fay Greene
Lisa Greenwald
Lisa Schulman
John Tytell

Poetry
Nikki Giovanni
Alison Granucci
David Hernandez
Ann Hudson
Zach Savich
Gary Soto

Science Fiction & Fantasy
Tahereh Mafi
Maureen McQuerry
Stephen Wallenfels

Short Story
Jena Barchas-Lichtenstein
Jesse Browner
Christopher Paul Curtis
Molly Hensley-Clancy
Leigh Stein
Thad Ziolkowski

Writing Portfolio
David Andersson
Coe Booth
Marjorie Celona
Major Jackson
Cordelia Jensen
Zoe Pagnamenta
Mike Romanos

EDITOR'S INTRODUCTION

Michaela Coplen

2013 National Student Poet

2014 Silver Medal with Distinction Portfolio Recipient

Scholastic Art & Writing Awards

> I do distrust the poet who discerns
> No character or glory in his times . . .
> If there's room for poets in this world
> A little overgrown, (I think there is)
> Their sole work is to represent the age,
> Their age . . . this live, throbbing age.
> —Elizabeth Barrett Browning, *Aurora Leigh*, 1856

Maybe Barrett Browning goes a little too far. I don't believe that you can say a poet's (or in our case, a writer's) "sole" work is anything specific—a writer's work is, simply: to see and learn and be and burn with everything. Still, she makes a valid point.

Elizabeth Barrett Browning wrote in an environment of immense social, economic, and artistic upheaval: Victorian England. Many of her peers created work based on mythological, religious, or historical narratives. They ignored the world in front of them, rejecting what they saw as the hard and unbeautiful nature of their rapidly industrializing age. Yet she persisted, using her voice and verse to reflect her age in all its complexity; she celebrated its energy and opportunity, but she also criticized the injustices of sexism, child labor, war, imperialism, and the continued practice of slavery in the United States.

All of this is to say: There are many aspects of our own age that are decidedly unbeautiful. It's often easier to turn away from the world and avoid confronting its injustices, to defer to long-established tradition, to quote Victorian poets when you're struggling with how to start your editor's introduction.

The writers in this book are braver than that.

Not only is their work exciting and original, not only does it exhibit technical skill and dedication to craft—it is also distinctly theirs. Their voices are clear and unafraid. Whether they are addressing racism, sexism, the criminal justice and education systems, foreign or domestic politics, environmental issues, economics, technology, or the age-old questions of life, death, and first dates, these writers are courageous and wise beyond their years. With timeless spirit, they represent the spirit of our time.

Let this book be a reminder: The simplest of tools are all it takes. Letters, words. Loose grammatical structure. Something to write with, something to write on. Some observation, some thought, some time. The writers included in this anthology have learned how to use these tools. They're surpassing the challenge laid down by Barrett Browning more than 150 years ago; in our overgrown world, these young writers are making room for themselves. And with their work, they're not only representing this live, throbbing age—they're changing it.

JACOB ADAMS, *Every Day Use*, Grade 12, Age 18. Stivers School for the Arts, Dayton, OH. Leah Stahl and Paula Willmot Kraus, *Educators*.

GOLD MEDAL PORTFOLIO

Graduating high school seniors may submit a portfolio of three to eight works for review by authors, educators, and literary professionals. Recipients of the Gold Medal Writing Portfolio receive a $10,000 scholarship.

Some of the writing selections have been excerpted. Visit **www.artandwriting.org/galleries** to read all of the work as it was submitted.

How to Do First Dates

RON ANAHAW, Grade 12, Age 17. George Washington Carver Center for Arts and Technology, Towson, MD. Suzanne Supplee, *Educator*

Bring several pounds of washcloths. Hide them. You're prone to sweat, and she's got skin like a glossy leaf. Don't be a cliché. When you compliment her, which is a must, stray from things like "You're pretty," or "You're beautiful," or "My God, you're so hot, damn, girl." That last one got you slapped. Hard. Your dignity faded faster than the mark on your face. Say things like "Your hips are the ocean's curves," or "Your eyes have stolen the stars tonight," or "Te amo. Tú tienes mi corazón." (Chicks dig Spanish.) Wait—scratch all that. Too creepy. Dial it down. Wait till you're married to say any of that. "You look nice tonight," that'll do just fine. If you feel so inclined, create hypotheticals in your mind of you two pumping out two-and-a-half kids, adopting a dog, and erecting a white picket fence in the suburbs, but by no means should you verbalize any of this. She's trying to enjoy her salad. You're at a diner, for God's sake. This is not the time or place to have a salad thrown at you in disgust. Even if you feel like your souls throb at the same wavelength, even if your lips are itching to pull apart and let loose a "We'resoulmateslet'sgetmarriedrightnow," resist. Resist. Focus on your burger. It's nice, tender beef. The fries go well with ketchup. Bite, chew, swallow, nod, laugh at her jokes. Plate's empty. Dessert. Yum. Wipe the sweat from your forehead. The stars giggle while you try small talk. Ask for water only if she does too. You don't want to seem *too* thirsty. You want to seem the *right* amount of thirsty. Oh no. Oh God, no. You notice that she has the kind of lips that wars are fought over. This is going to be tough. *"Are you enjoying the apple pie?"* Good, a question; it will distract you from her lips. Anyway. She has no idea the factors that affect your answer. For example: Is she enjoying it? Is it warm or cold? Have you used your fork or spoon or— God forbid—your *hand* to eat it? How big is it? Does it make your lips itch? Wipe your hands, you're sweating. Say the pie is fine, that's safe. Your tongue is so parched—*hold. Don't ask for water.* Dessert is done. She's still talking to you. She doesn't care that the food is done. *My God, you've made it this far.* Keep it cool. Don't worry, you're smooth, you're slick, you know how to spin a few cool rhymes. "I'm chillin' in a diner / with a cool girl, I like her / almost as much as this apple pie / hope she likes this nervous guy."

. . . What. Did. You. Just. Do. Yeah, that's right, inwardly groan at the pure cheesiness of what you just said! In fact, outwardly groan! You idiot! You—*"Was that a love rap?"* She's smiling. She's giggling. Wait. Maybe you didn't just screw up. My friend, you can do it. Lean in for the kiss. Do it.

Letters I Have Yet to Send

EDIL HASSAN, Grade 12, Age 17. Burlington Senior High School, Burlington, VT. Eve Tyrrell-Berinati, *Educator*

I. Dear Somalia,
We didn't think it would happen. We didn't ask for any of this,
to have to swallow our language to make room for a new one,
for our names, to be chopped in two,
our histories, reduced to identification cards.
We may never have asked for this, but neither did we ask to see you fall apart,
to gag and retch until we were heaved out of you,
a migration of violence spilling from the borders of your mouth.
It's been 17 years since I saw you last, and I've cried enough tears
to fill the ocean that separates us three times over.

II. Dear Zelia,
I saw thousands climb aboard your boats.
Thin, brown ankles stepping over the side,
their belongings reduced to small wads in their arms,
smelling of smoke and burnt wheat.

I saw my cousin there too.
It was when he gave up on you,
saw something less cruel on the horizon. I can't remember his
face.
But I remember when the boat turned over,
when your ocean filled his lungs with water.
I used to love the sea, but I can't look at the water now
without seeing his bloated body bobbing at the surface.

III. Dear Berbera,
They asked about you at the deportation center.
I wanted to tell them that you are how I go to sleep every
night,
how your smile may be like an open wound, but it's the only
one you have left,
and that it still makes you look beautiful.
But all that came out, as I pressed a shaking finger to
your name on a long list, was: This is where I became a refugee.

IV. Dear Moqdishu,
You are why I see home in bones and things that fall apart.
Why I stiffen at the blaring drone of airplanes overhead,
a phantom hum in my ears as if a bomb is about to drop.
I can't sleep without thinking of
your dark alleys, and smoke-filled skies.
I can see you in the thick lines that run across my
grandmother's face,
in the crease at her brow, around her wilting mouth.
She stopped smiling because of you.
So to answer the question you asked first all those years ago,
and that you ask now, no.
I can't. You've hurt me too badly.

V. Dear Borama,
I see you everywhere.
In long car rides, when I am moments away from falling asleep,
my mind drifting away as if I am being lulled by your countless hills.
I can feel you in the softness of wooden rosary beads,
your laugh in my morning prayer,
your smile in the way my supplications
tumble from my heavy mouth. With your winding streets of red dust,
and your skies that are bright even in the dark,
you make me yearn
for a home that was never really mine to begin with.

To Mayor Bill de Blasio

TRACE DEPASS, Grade 12, Age 16. Thomas A. Edison Career and Technical High School, Jamaica, NY. Patrick Lagmay, *Educator*

Dear Bill de Blasio,

You tell us to stop "resisting arrest." Now, are you referring to the way we do 24/7, or do you just mean living when you say "resisting arrest"? I wonder if this is what you would tell Dante. A son, no matter if he owned a gun or had a reason for "suspicion" besides his pigment, a color we know all too well . . . too bad. Make sure to let your children know that this is the way it is, next time. Rear fear, if you're morally sound with the idea that lives can end unfinished as ellipses, or like those "stolen" cigars . . . or that Arizona . . . or the last breath still pleading the fifth and for his life at the same time in a chokehold, somewhere . . . In America, a black boy is going unfinished. But you say stop resisting arrest as if you're compelled to say so, as if you were the one under arrest and weren't even told why, as if you had the right to remain silent rather than accountable for a department for the city you govern, like politicians properly represent those who got them where they are, or something . . .

Like you were dying here with us,
the black community.

Subjects and Predicates

ALEXIS PAYNE, Grade 12, Age 17. Pittsburgh CAPA 6-12, A Creative and Performing Arts Magnet, Pittsburgh, PA. Mara Cregan, *Educator*

1. I am. She is. He is. It is. We are. They are. They go. We go. She learns. He learns. I—

2. Fifty-two tiles made the length across the classroom floor. He had counted. And the pencil sharpener made a whirring sound like a half-dead bug writhing on a windowsill. Her lipstick flaunted light pink like pomegranate seeds, rosy red staining her bright, white front teeth. Outside a bird tapped its beak on the glass and the teacher with the strawberry candy lips ran her finger along the chalkboard and talked about nouns or predicates or adverbs. To him, her words sounded like falling hail or crackling bacon. She merely floated on the edge of relevance, in her heavy brown skirt, her cream-colored tunic, her pale skin stained with dark age spots. He sat in the back of the class with a book bag full of 25-cent candy from the drug store near his house. While the rest of the world bathed in Standard English, he sucked on Hot Tamales and estimated how many pieces of candy he would have to sell to buy a loaf of white bread and a can of powdered milk.

3. Ruben. Ruben. Ruben. His arms are black and his lips are blue. Ruben. Ruben. Ruben. Come here, little boy who can't spell *two*. Ruben. Ruben. Ruben.

4. At lunchtime he climbed to the roof of the school. He made castles out of rocks and imagined himself in them.

5. We ain't never been ones to beg. Ain't gonna start now none. Somebody try to hand you something. You say you just fine, you hear me? Only the poor take handouts. And we ain't poor.

6. P-o-o-r. You know what that spells? You know what that spells? You know what that spells? What about b-l-a-c-k? That's a color. Spell it with me? Come on now, b-l-a-c-k. You know the word run? Spell that for me, huh? R-U-N. Good. Good. Good.

7. This mother's a heroin addict or something. The father's nowhere to be found.

8. Classic.

9. Any other family?

10. None, as far as I can tell.

11. The boy needs help. Some special class. He can hardly read at all.

12. That's not my job.

13. Not my job.

14. Not my job.

15. FLY. Spell fly for me? Fly? You know what flies? Birds fly. Planes fly.

16. He hardly talks, the boy. He has no friends.

17. Where's he eat? Does he eat at all?

18. The castle was thirty rocks tall and fifty rocks wide and he made little rooms and beds and light fixtures out of grass. It sat on the edge of the roof and if one looked closely they could see the steeple he had placed on the top. He collected ants, and he put them in the rooms and they never had to learn to read or write. He would sing to them, quietly of course, and he would try to make them sit in rows and learn their numbers.

19. Boy, if you don't learn nothin' you better learn how to count good, you hear me? If you can count, you can rule the world. Like the president.

20. He's a dead duck, you know? The boy. He's in the third grade, and he's still reading like a kindergartner.

21. He sits on the roof during lunchtime.

22. There's nothing to it. Just pass him on.

23. Pass him on? But he can hardly read.

24. Read. Read. Read.

25. You've got to read, boy. Else they gonna flunk you.

26. The ants don't know how to read.

27. Ain't nobody talkin' bout no ants. We talkin' bout you, boy.

28. He smashed his castle on the roof and wrote R-U-N all over it in black sharpie.

But I Didn't Do Anything

AMELIA ROSKIN-FRAZEE, Grade 12, Age 18. Lick-Wilmerding
High School, San Francisco, CA. Robin Von Breton, *Educator*

The American legal system generally punishes actions that cause harm, but not inactions or omissions of action that cause harm, except in special circumstances. The child's plea of "But I didn't do anything" is codified in centuries of American jurisprudence. I believe that the failure to act to prevent serious bodily injury to another, when action can be taken without probable danger to the actor, should be criminal.

As it stands, I can watch another person pass out facedown and drown in a two-inch puddle of water in front of me on the sidewalk. I can even cackle with sadistic pleasure watching her drown, but I have no culpability if I fail to do minimal actions to save her from her fate, because the law of omissions gives people a legal right to not intervene in such situations.

The American law of omissions runs contrary to what is near unanimity of moral reasoning. Absent more information about the passed-out victim (e.g., she is, in the moral reasoning cliché, Hitler's mother), social utility would be served from an intervention. We would will that all rational sentient beings intervene to help. In designing a world a priori with reflection, we would design rules to require assistance, lest we be the one in need. Thus, Mill, Kant, and Rawls could sit down for a beer and enjoy a moment of agreement on a position. I suspect most non-philosopher views of morality would agree as well, whether informed by various religious beliefs or centuries of convergence on what is common decency. Even behavioral biologists might see the virtues of the brain chemistry bath after an act of altruism. Many other countries, including Denmark, Russia, and Italy, require that citizens take action in a situation where a person needs help. If there is such a thing as a common moral consensus, this is it.

The failure of the law to identify and enforce these core values threatens the integrity of the legal system. If the law does not follow the American ethical code, does not that make the law unethical? How are we supposed to respect the law if it is unethical? Why should we adhere to it at all? If the law neither protects people in society nor holds everyone to the same basic ethical standard we strive to uphold in our communities, what is its purpose?

It is also deeply American to see ourselves as invulnerable, always responsible for misfortune that befalls us, and blame those who need help. While condoning omissions gives respect to the American value of freedom, condoning omissions sanctions a dangerous, self-serving society and draws a troublesome line between our ethical and legal codes, undermining the value of both.

So, why do we not punish omissions?

First, we zealously defend against any encroachment on personal liberty and individual freedom, no matter how illusory the threat. We value the individual's right to remain a solitary, isolated actor with no responsibility to others. A person may choose to save someone helpless but shall never be commanded to do so. We might condemn her if she lets the widow or orphan drown, but we will never punish her failure. It would be un-American. A pathological fear of tyranny prevents basic legislation on simple matters of moral decency. Although all law is a codification of some moral system, we should have a healthy skepticism about moral claims to legislation, as many such claims reinforce substantive inequality or codify narrow religious or minority views. However, where we have clear, neutral rules that reinforce general civic action, such concerns are unfounded.

Similarly, we might fear the risk of liability should someone act. In administering CPR as a trained paramedic, I might crack the victim's rib. In recent years, some states have passed Good Samaritan laws that encourage people to assist others by protecting them from prosecution or tort liability if something goes wrong with their effort to help. Any system that requires good faith actions should not punish those very actions.

Where obligations to act do exist, they primarily do because of a concept of duty. Parents, teachers, and caretakers must take action in a situation where the person they have pledged to look after is in danger. In other words, a relationship can change whether or not a person has a right to omit a helpful action. While I have the right to watch my neighbor's child collapse from a seizure without doing anything to help, my neighbor does not have that right.

Further, the law now also states that persons are not allowed to omit a helpful action if they created the dangerous situations in the first place. By creating the moral hazard, one assumes a responsibility for the danger posed.

Finally, one may, by virtue of a commercial or business relationship, have a duty to assist another. A paid caretaker cannot watch me die. A related concept is that certain professionals, such as doctors, may have a duty to patients in their care.

I understand our deference to individual freedom, but omissions are so fundamentally at odds with compassion and communal responsibility. Omissions deny us protection; we are on our own, not protected by the community around us. Why do we accept that we have no duty to each other? Why do we not understand that we may not always be vulnerable, but we might find ourselves in situations where we are and require the help of another? Why would we want to design a system so at odds with enlightened self-interest?

Community may be easier to create when it is homogenous racially and otherwise, but not so easy when filled with "others." Ironically, America's inclusiveness of various people (whether involuntarily imported, conquered, or otherwise) may have defeated our very ability to form a meaningful sense of community.

Any attempt to legislate omissions would likely generate an enormous backlash, cast in the usual news outlets as a treacherous destruction of treasured civil liberties, another chapter in the inevitable death march to tyranny. But it is false to see omissions as a case of freedom. All rights have limits when they pose grave harm to others. Just as the freedom of speech does not allow a person to place others in danger by shouting fire in a crowded theater, the freedom to not act should not allow a person to omit actions when doing so places others in danger. What if the theater is on fire, which you alone see, and then you leave and do not bother to tell anyone else, condemning others in the theater to potentially die in the inferno? It is only by distinguishing action and culpable inaction that the distinction makes sense.

We should move to an understanding that we are responsible for people beyond just those attached to us biologically or contractually. Our idea of community as a larger group of people who help one another is undermined by the law that condones the opposite.

It is precisely the failure to have a general duty to another person that undermines a basic core value of community. Laws should serve to reinforce our better selves, creating a morality that emphasizes that which makes us better. One can spend hours drafting all the nuances of actual legislative wording of my proposal, but the basic core structure would create over time a generational shift in what is acceptable behavior, redefining what we owe each other and ourselves.

Sacrament

MONIQUE TAYLOR, Grade 12, Age 17. Saginaw Arts and Sciences Academy, Saginaw, MI. Rebekah Rogers, *Educator*

Break open my ribcage,
stick a hand in,
the Word is in there somewhere.
Wrench organs,
pierce flesh,
find stress in a heartbeat.
My veins are building a temple,
foreign invaders piloting flesh.
Be rough,
crack fingernails,
find perfection in a rearview mirror
and the eyeliner smeared onto a pillow.
Bury me in fleece
and drink hope from a coffee cup.

I am an architect,
lungs filled with shingles and wires
but it doesn't matter what shell I call home
because we were all born in the earth,
filthy and degraded.
We were honesty,
hid ourselves in bushes
and clothed ourselves to hide our shame.
This isn't your Eden.
I'll never get back to that place,
no matter how much I vomit
or sip watered-down wine

to cleanse the taste of fruit
from my mouth.

You promised me a haven.
Look where we are now,
stuck in a vacant parking lot
overdosing on forgiveness
and breaking stained-glass windows.
I'll buy a confessional,
kneel in it, and say my Hail Marys
with a rosary clutched in my fist.
Run for years,
that's my penance.
I've broken promises
but can't figure out why
I'm stuck on train tracks
with the engine running.
I've got both feet on the dashboard
and a Bible in the backseat
for a bit of light reading.

Two Months In

HANNAH RICHTER, Grade 12, Age 18. Miami Palmetto Senior High School, Miami, FL. Jason Meyers, *Educator*

Two months in and still
no sign of rescue.
I've been starving here,
between ideas
for so long
that the ribs between
my lines of prose
are beginning to
show.

In survival situations
they tell you to use
what you have. Well,
I've got a
ballpoint pen
and a collection of
semi-melodic sentence
fragments,
none of which can
save my life.

My hands are blistered
from rubbing old ideas
together, hoping for a
spark,
or even a little
smoke
to awaken the adrenaline

sleeping inside
what's left of my head.

When they find my body
out here,
I hope they notice the way
I am holding the pen, like
a cross,
or more hopeful like
kindling.

Saving It for Later

GRANT MCCLURE, Grade 12, Age 18. South Carolina Governor's School for the Arts and Humanities, Greenville, SC. Mamie Morgan and Scott Gould, *Educators*

Climb up the brick steps onto the porch. Ring the doorbell. Wait for me to answer. Follow me into the foyer. Be sure to take note of the hardwood floors scuffed from years of baseball cleats. You may wish to get a closer look at the upright piano, but don't bother. No one in the family ever learned to finger its keys, and it means nothing to me other than a place to set down a book. Instead, open the door beneath the stairwell to your left. Inside you'll find those same cleats, a five-gallon bucket full of baseballs, my father's tired glove, my lefty first-baseman's mitt, an Easton composite bat, and a more primitive wooden Louisville Slugger.

For years my mother's tried to get rid of my baseball equipment, and for years my father and I have protested. He used to leave work early to drive me to a sandlot on John's Island for practice, and when my batting average nosedived, to a hitting coach in Summerville. We watched the Braves play on Sunday after church. Other times we played catch in the backyard, the steady metronome of those laced-leather balls snapping in the webbing of our gloves. We don't play anymore. I quit baseball in ninth grade in favor of basketball and girls. Close the door. Follow me into the living room.

You may take interest in the gaudy floral wallpaper, but it was installed by the previous homeowners—a fragment of a history not my own. Instead, focus your eyes on the shelf below the television, where my baby album swells with photographs, hospital papers, elementary school report cards, diary entries, lost teeth, snippets of the past that mean nothing to me, but everything to my mother. She needs a reminder that her 6'5" son, who now struggles to say *Love you too, bye* before hanging up, once hugged her around her knees, ate chocolate cake with his bare hands, refused to wear anything but his father's hard hat and a pair of tightie whities. If the house were to catch on fire, this book is the first thing she'd grab. Now close the album, and follow me into the dining room.

Don't be fooled by the antique grain of the dining room table. My mother bought it on sale at IKEA. Instead, take a closer look at the china cabinet in the back corner of the room. Don't even think about opening the glass doors—don't even breathe. Study each ornate bowl, platter, chalice, vase. Years ago, my great-great-grandmother's antebellum hands perhaps poured herself a glass of sweet tea from the slender crystal pitcher. This cabinet contains relics of my family's past best left untouched, better observed from a distance with a crooked neck. Take three slow steps back. Follow me up the stairwell.

Bypass my parents' room. Walk down the hallway until you reach my bedroom on the right. Open my closet and you'll find a stack of quilts. Unfold the top quilt, a Dutchman's Puzzle sewn by my Aunt Tracy, and my rock collection tumbles to the floor. The collection started in the third grade with a chunk of granite I stole from Rocko's Countertops in North Charleston. It was just lying there on the concrete floor, a lonely island broken away from the mainland of a larger slab. From there my collection blossomed: shards of flint, seashells fossilized in limestone, burnt pieces of charcoal that stained my hands black. For almost a year I was terrified my parents would excavate my collection—that I was somehow violating a moral code by stealing from the earth.

When my parents discovered the collection, they didn't scold me. Quite the opposite. They began to shower me with all things rock: geology books, catalogs on mining, laminated pamphlets that opened like road maps. If I made good grades my father drove me to Black Water Minerals on Market Street. Any kind of rock I wanted, they had. Tourmaline, rose quartz, citrine, amethyst, peridot, aquamarine, tiger's eye, turquoise, figurines of toads carved from sandstone, even dream catchers, which aren't rocks at all. When I sort through these boxes, I'm reminded of a time when holding something shiny in my palm was enough to make me happy.

Skirt around my bed to the left side of the room, where you'll find my desk drawers overflowing with chartreuse bucktails, golden pheasant necks, 1/0 hooks, spools of flat waxed nylon knotted together—the results of my middle school obsession with fly tying. At the height of my addiction, I stopped bringing friends to my room because I feared they might not associate with me after seeing the rabbit pelt I used for tying Hare's Ear Nymphs. Fly tying was a more practical addiction than rocks: It fostered patience, attention to detail. Lessons I remind myself every time I fidget in a chair, ready to move on to the next thing.

Get a better look at the tall dresser pushed up against the right wall. If you wipe your hand on top of this dresser, you'll find dust. If you keep reaching, you'll find an old chest filled with sports headlines from the newspaper, comic strips, church pamphlets. Keep searching until you find a slip of paper from a fortune cookie, the words *A Hen's Beak Is Better Than Ox's Tail* printed on it in red ink.

I'm not entirely sure what this proverb means, but I know exactly why I couldn't bring myself to throw it away with the rest of my takeout meal. I'd just broken up with my girlfriend and was looking for any kind of advice or answer I could get— even if I didn't understand it. I needed something or someone to get my mind off the pair of polka-dot socks she bought me for my birthday, the letter tucked underneath my mattress, her heavy black script, the strand of her hair clinging to the collar of my winter coat. And I still need it. You can close the box now.

By now you've noticed the map of the Whale Branch River hanging above my bed. Where I spent my summers growing up. Where I once clubbed a baby blacktip shark to death. Where I pulled a crab trap up by its slimy rope and stuffed the lifeless animal inside to use as bait. This map is a constant reminder of that evening, the scuttling blue crabs, the air rancid with rotting chicken thighs—yet I can't take it off the wall.

If, instead of holding on to these things—instead of hoarding rocks, fly tying materials, sporting goods, photographs, newspaper articles, church bulletins, letters, memories—my family forgot about it all, would we somehow be less human? Instead of unfolding a quilt, scanning the top of a dresser, opening up a book, a cabinet, would I forget where I came from? Would I, instead of slipping that fortune into my pocket, go off on a walk and never come back? There's happiness and there's sadness, things I never want to let go, things that I want to let go, but can't. There's saving it for later, filing it all away for a while so in five years, twenty years, a hundred years, I might open them back up again and remember who I was, who I am, how far I've come from boyhood obsessions, from killing that shark, from loving that girl. Let me walk you to your car.

ZACHARY SEGER, *Blood Landscape*, Grade 12, Age 17. New Canaan High School, New Canaan, CT. Jeanne McDonagh, *Educator*.

GOLD, SILVER, AMERICAN VOICES, AND SPONSORED AWARDS

Students in grades 7–12 may submit works in 11 writing categories. This year nearly 3,100 writing submissions that were awarded Gold Keys at the regional level were reviewed by authors, educators, and literary professionals. Gold, Silver, and American Voices Medals were awarded to works that demonstrated originality, technical skill, and emergence of a personal voice.

Sponsored Awards recognize works that are the best in their grade level (Best-in-Grade Award), or deal with issues such as tolerance (Gedenk Award for Tolerance) or technology and privacy (Creativity & Citizenship Award).

Some of the writing selections have been excerpted. Visit **www.artandwriting.org/galleries** to read all of the work as it was submitted.

What Not to Do When Taking BART

CATHERINE GAO, Grade 11, Age 16. Leland High School, San Jose, CA.
Jennifer Touchton, *Educator*

A week ago, I sat on a BART car in uncomfortable silence for forty-five minutes. Thirty other strangers sat around me, each diligently doing the exact same thing: nothing. Half stared vacantly at the walls of the car, stopping every few minutes to glance down at their phones. The other half snored gently with their faces smushed against the windows. I closed my eyes and tried to disappear into my seat.

This wasn't a new experience for me. I knew the drill: Keep your head down, don't make eye contact, draw as little attention to yourself as humanly possible. I also knew that not everyone followed the rules: Once in a while, a Wal-Mart worker would saunter in, complaining loudly about the expired pickle he found in his hamburger, or a man decked out in running gear would sprint into the car and start doing pull-ups on the metal bars that ran across the ceiling. Whenever this happened, the other passengers gravitated quickly toward the other end of the car, leaving an empty circle of seats around the disruption. But aside from the oddities, everybody followed an unspoken code: Don't see and don't be seen, and nobody will bother you. It was an efficient system. People passed in and out of the cars with barely a glance back, never stopping to realize that, behind them, thirty other humans rode home to their lives and their families. As for me, I did my part to avoid as many people as possible.

I only broke the code once, and it was on account of the Beyoncé man. He walked onto BART one day—beanie drooping, pants sagging, oversized Beatles T-shirt battered by the wind—with a shiny silver radio blasting "Single Ladies" by Beyoncé. I could feel the judgmental stares of thirty collared-shirt-wearing engineer parents simultaneously boring into his back. He sprawled himself across the seat meant for the handicapped, cranked up the volume, and proceeded to butcher the song, delivering an obnoxiously off-key rendition in front of an appalled group of BART passengers.

He sang for about four minutes, during which time I found myself on the opposite end of the BART car, trying to squeeze past two middle-aged men for a window seat. It took a while, but I managed—and ended up triumphantly sandwiched between a stranger and the wall. I sat in silence. The singing continued. I looked up and saw that the two middle-aged men I had just displaced were eyeing the singer with suspicion. Self-consciously, they began tugging at their collars and checking to make sure their shirts were still tucked into their pants, as if simply sharing the same BART car with a rebellious teenager would somehow tarnish their professional image. Not that it mattered; professional or not, on public transportation they were nothing more than faces to forget.

In hindsight, I'm not too sure why I chose the company of two balding thirty-year-olds over someone who, despite lacking in vocal ability, seemed to exude something nobody else had: confidence. I watched him singing from the other end of the car, and the entire time I was debating whether or not to approach him. The idea, of course, was ludicrous; all my mom's advice about stranger danger kept running through my head—and besides, if I got up and returned to my original seat near Mr. Beyoncé, I would face disapproval from the legion of engineer parents who stood packed together, army-style, on the other side. I wasn't about to lead the exodus from suffocating boredom into the promised land of teenage disobedience and freedom of song. I was no Moses.

Still, he seemed quirky and interesting. But while I was testing the idea in my head, the BART pulled into the 12th Street Oakland Station and the man, still singing, walked out with his radio.

It took me a while to piece together what it was about him that was so intriguing, but I found it eventually: He was real. Even in public, he refused to degrade himself into a shadow. He was himself, and if others couldn't handle him, that was their problem. People—including me—moved out of the way because he seemed inconsiderate. Was he? Maybe it wasn't his problem; maybe it was ours.

Sometimes I wonder how much I miss on BART every time I choose to stare out the window while deliberately ignoring the person sitting across from me. I usually interact with those around me in the same way that I ride public transportation: as briefly and as nonchalantly as possible. I forget the guilt I felt when a friend I had passed by every day in the hallway, but never stopped to talk to, broke down in the middle of eighth-grade English class because her father lay dying in a hospital room. I forget my horror when, two months ago, my best friend called to inform me that a classmate of his, who I had seen around campus but never approached, was contemplating suicide because she felt lost and alone. I forget that, five years ago, when I walked onto my middle school campus with my head bowed down and my bony shoulders scrunched up underneath a backpack, I would have given anything to have someone approach me and ask how I was doing, so I could finally tell them that I was anorexic.

People aren't meant to be avoided. People are meant to be understood, appreciated, and loved. Caught up in the frantic race to fit in, to look polished and forgettable, to travel from point A to point B as efficiently as possible, I forgot that those around me are not empty holograms and should not be treated as such.

Who was that BART singer? I still think about him sometimes—where was he heading on BART? He was a horrendous singer, but maybe he was a talented actor, or a cook, or a boyfriend. Maybe he, too, had once lost relatives, or seen friends get hurt, or kept a secret that ate away at his self-confidence. He was unconventional and he was different; he was a reminder that nobody is ever merely another face in the crowd.

22-Mile Graveyard:
Moore, Oklahoma

MAYA LEW, Grade 11, Age 16. ACES Educational Center for the Arts, New Haven, CT. Caroline Rosenstone, *Educator*

1.

The tornado left everything broken but the toolshed. The townspeople plucked slugs off the side-panels for days afterward, old wood peeling like rotten bananas. River water ripped past the edges of the stream, they fixed torn seams with mud and rocks (double knots, triple knots), pipes from broken under-sinks. The sunflowers floated, facedown, river trout halfway to belly-up.

2.

Exactly two months and three days after the tornado, the twelve of us arrive in Moore, Oklahoma. We unload from crisp-cold airplane cabins, twelve Jewish teenagers with New England skin foreign to hundred-and-something degree summers, and eyes that had never seen so many miles of nothing. The first thing we learn: There is no dirt in Oklahoma, just clay. Red clay (really red) that stains the soles of our shoes and sticks to under-nail tissue. We are so careful to *scrubscrubscrub*, but somehow it still creaks in the beds of our teeth. Our first day, in a museum, they tell us it gets its color from the blood of natives long spilled. The land remembers what people forget.

3.

We unload from our rental vans at the mouth of a one-way street.

The counselors say to us, "Welcome to your new home!"

For the entire summer, our piece of the Moore mosaic is 184 to 626 Ledges Lane. Mim, Sarah, and I are assigned number 192, a ranch-style brick, open-roofed, wooden braces clawing at the sky.

We start by separating the gangrenous before it spreads, hefting garbage bags of crumbled bricks, edges crusted with the last of mortar. The day after, we disinfect. Later, we suture, staunch the blood that escapes our sloppy stitches, and then, at last, we build.

4.

Morning, first day on the work site: *We didn't have a storm cellar, so we huddled in the back of my car and watched out the smudged-up windows. I remember seeing the other car get scooped up and flung away, and my daughters were both wailing. I saw the mouth of the big thing, the jaws and the back-molars and everything. It just took the cornfield in one gulp. Four months and my entire income in one swallow.*

5.

We shower communally in the local Y. The first time, all naked and fleshy-pink, we slink into corners, staring at the tiles underfoot and wishing we could slide into the grout. A tap on my shoulder startles me and I turn around. A girl (*Miriam, but call me Mim, and also I'm from Rhode Island)* stands next to me.

"Is there clay on my back?" she asks.

And there is. Her back is brushed red, and I nod and scrub her raw then ask, "Me?"

She nods and rubs a layer of red off my shoulder in sure circles. Another girl—Sarah, New Jersey, *One thing about me is I love America*—asks, "What about me?" And soon we are scrubbing, and surrounded by each other, knocking elbows at first but we find slots to slip into, clicking gears into place. The red pools at our feet as we shed sleeves of Oklahoma clay, letting the land lap between our toes and then weep down the drain.

6.

A luncheon for those we are building for, all survivors, all timid. We share smiles and eye the clock, small-talking over plates of al dente pasta. Each table is for a different house. Number 192, the house Sarah, Mim, and I are working on, is the only empty table.

"I'm sorry," the program director tells us and hands us a newspaper, crackling and cratered by creases, as if run through the dryer while crumpled up. The headline reads: DISASTER IN MOORE, 4 DEAD, 56 INJURED.

The four empty folding chairs around our table sit like stones in the stomach of this room.

7.

Day seven: I am sitting, back flat against the sun, eating lunch on a roof I built myself. Peanut butter caught in the ridges of my thumbprints, nails clanking in my pocket, I face miles of churned-up land. Regurgitated houses lie silent, still. Chewed up, spit out, left to dry. I am flanked by the broken houses. All around me: people slathering layers of thick paint over harsh scars, splinting fractured laundry room femurs, and shuffling the last of last year under scratchy-new rugs.

I think of the way we fit. I think we are too bright and too new for the scene before us. We are still in the box, cased in hard plastic, arms zip-tied to a cardboard backdrop of a sunny beach. The wooden cartilage of doorframes and bedroom bones stripped to the marrow stir in the lazy breeze as the sun heaves upwards. The landscape of carcasses marbles onward for miles and miles.

Across the street, a vulture scratches his beak on the clavicle of a two-family and then flies away.

8.

At our home, there are three chickens on the counter soaking in a tub of water. The only kosher chicken in all of Oklahoma, and they're whole.

Sarah, Mim, and I end up butchering them because no one else knows how. We crack ribcages with a hollow thud and slip our fingers underneath. We pry off cartilage, milky-white bone caps that snap in our palms, and pull out coils of ropey intestines, salted-slug lungs, and a liver like a deflated car tire.

We know what it is to destroy. Breathe in, break down, and pile hearts into the trash can, listen to make sure there is no noise.

9.

Week two: We confront the toolshed. The door is persistent, and when we pull it open, the shed sighs, sagging a little on its warped foundation. Inside there are three sleeping bags, plastered over with insulation crumbled like leftover cicada shells.

In the corner, a bird's nest is lodged into the torn stomach of a teddy bear. The vulture's nest.

"We should go," Sarah says, but I am staring out of the window. The window with the busted panes, as if punched through with a giant fist. The window that overlooks number 192 Ledges Lane.

"They saw it happen," I say. From the corner, a baby vulture peeps.

10.
And when it's all done, there is still a patchy seam through the middle of the house if you squint and lean and frown enough. I want to pick at the parted brick lips until the skin of the whole thing peels off and all that's left is a drywall skeleton. We should've started from scratch. The kitchen floor still buckles under running toddler feet, and I can only ever see the curtains thrashing in a violent wind.

11.
In the bathroom of the Y, I scour until soap seeps past my skin. I step out of the shower, but I still feel wrong.

At our makeshift home, there is no full-length mirror, just three small mirrors puttied onto the wall in a line. There, I stare at myself in three parts, a Maya sonata. Head to chest, torso to hips, legs and more legs. I can't piece myself together. I feel disjointed, awkward, some Picasso gone bad.

Sarah and Mim are behind me.

"We shouldn't be here," I tell them.

"We don't have to be at dinner until seven-thirty," Sarah says, and I shake my head.

"No," I say, "here, Oklahoma. We don't belong."

"Why not?" Sarah says.

"Everyone else is building a sanctuary, and we're building a tomb," I say.

"We're not building a tomb," Mim says, "we're building a memorial."

12.
Day fifteen: There are eleven others on the roof, eleven other teenagers crazy enough to throw away half a summer of mistakes and *that time* to travel to Oklahoma. We perch on the roof, mouths full of peanut butter and the weight of stories for later suckered to the flat of our tongues. We eat in rhythm, our arms cycling through CRUST then APPLE then WATER in unison. To my right, Mim hefts wood planks onto cement floors. To the left, Sarah fans mulch over the front yard of a three-bedroom, punching holes every few feet for shrubs and trees.

I watch, overhead, the V of a vulture's wings beating backwards from our single street. And I think: *not broken, but healing.*

13.
The sunlight fans out off the glass into scalpel-straight slices. The blue and green and red shards curl into petals, curl into soft crow's feet. The edge of the glass pieces curve into thick vines, then branch out into flat petals that outline the slope of a chin. A face made of flowers made of hundreds of different fractured beer bottles. The glass Gandhi covers the back of a hunched gas station, three streets down from number 192, blossoming cheeks burning up over the burnt-out city.

LISSETTE BUSTAMANTE, *My Garden*, Photography.
Grade 11, Age 16. Chicago High School for the Arts,
Chicago, IL. Catarina Araujo, *Educator.*

The Other

KIMAYA LECAMWASAM, Grade 10, Age 16. BASIS Scottsdale, Scottsdale, AZ. Angela Ackerman and Lyndsay Haag, *Educators.*
American Voices Award

I am the color of worn cardboard. Of a corkboard. Of the cover of my Bob Dylan singles sleeves songbook. It has dogged me my entire life. They have called me "the Other," even though I was born in America. Even though I laugh, cry, scream, dream in English and only English. Even though I have been pledging allegiance to the flag of the United States of America for my entire life.

They have told me to go back to where I come from. Where? I come from a one-room apartment in Boston, Massachusetts; from a little yellow house where I believed fairies hid within the skirts of rose petals; from a green house on a hill overlooking evergreen forests and a bright-blue sky; from a neighborhood in Scottsdale, Arizona, where brown and black and white were just colors and neighbors were neighbors were neighbors.

But they do not care about that, do they? I am different. I am "Other." Do I belong?

I was four when I was told that I was too dark to be a princess. At recess on a cool spring day in Massachusetts, all of the little girls were holding court in a pile of damp woodchips.

They sat as daintily as they possibly could, with thin strips of wood poking and pricking their legs and a deep dampness seeping through their pink skirts. They were blonde. And pale. I remember that much clearly. I sat awkwardly at the edge of the circle, trying to blend in. I desperately wanted to blend in. And I wanted to be Belle.

Belle was my favorite princess. She read, and she dreamed, and her library was fantastic. I liked to imagine that her shelves were full of row upon row of *Magic Tree House* books and picture books and adventure stories like the ones my parents would read to me before bed. The Woodchip Court told me that I could not be Belle because Belle did not look like me. She was the color of snow, and I was the color of dirt. They grudgingly offered me the role of Jasmine in their magical kingdom of stereotypes. I grudgingly accepted because I wanted friends. I hated Jasmine; I was afraid of tigers and stomach-revealing tops and genies.

When I was six, my grandmother held her frail arm up against mine and scolded me for how dark my skin had become. I had spent my summer with my nose practically squashed into the rough pavement, observing fat and fuzzy caterpillars as they lazily wriggled around in the warm sun that filtered down on Middle-of-Nowhere, Massachusetts. Kickball and bike races and adventuring were summer traditions. Dense woods surrounded my neighborhood, and everyone would spend hours wading in streams, searching for arrowheads and pretending to be pilgrims. But sweet summer days came at a cost. I was even darker now, the color of tree bark, molasses, mud. Fair was beautiful. My grandmother was fair. She proudly told me that she was as pale as the day she was born, that she never left the house without an umbrella, that the sun's evil rays never had the chance to make her look different, make her look like me. For my birthday in the fall, she gave me a tube of sunblock and a wide-brimmed hat.

I was ten when I was told that I could not be anything other than a servant girl. I had dreamt of going to Broadway, of being a star, of my name in lights. I went to music classes, tried to act, sought advice from every possible avenue. The words of Dorothy Loudon were the gospel. My music teacher was an active member of the Arizona musical theater scene, and I hero-worshiped her. She was blonde and pale and perfect, just like I wanted to be. We talked about my chances on Broadway. She sat me down and smiled at me and told me that my best hope of a role would be a servant girl in *The King and I* because of my color. And casting directors just do not hire people who don't look right, sweetie . . .

At sixteen, I saw the cycle begin again. My five-year-old cousin fell madly in love with *Frozen* and had an Elsa-themed birthday party, Halloween costume, holiday party. She is just as brown as I am, as brown as worn cardboard. She believes she looks just like Elsa and, right now, her little friends do too. They do not seem to care that she is the darkest of them all. She is so innocent, they all are. When does this go wrong? When does color become all we see? When will she lose her right to be a princess, to play in the yard, to be a star? My one wish is for her to be a princess forever. But castles crumble and crowns fall.

Over and over again I have been told that I do not belong here, that I am the Other. But I do not belong out there, either. I eat rice with a fork, I have never worn a sari in my life, I listen to the Beatles, I do not speak any other language. I am American, born and raised. And if I do not belong here, do not belong there, do I belong anywhere?

I am still waiting to find out.

Pulp Nonfiction

NAMAN AGARWAL, Grade 10, Age 15. William Fremd High School, Palatine, IL. Colene Brockman, *Educator*

Slaughterhouse 5, or "So It Goes"
December 28, 2012

It was a halfhearted attempt, really. Come on, half a bottle of *liquid* Tylenol? And it wasn't even regular Tylenol, it was Children's Tylenol! For someone considered nerdy enough to tell you about the chemical makeup of acetaminophen (N-[4-hydroxyphenyl]ethanamide, if you were wondering) and the actual dosage of "Cherry Blast Children's Tylenol" required to destroy a thirteen-year-old's liver, it was just . . . weak. It's like watching someone fill in random blanks on a standardized test just because "it's not for a grade." Except it's not like that at all, because in that case, it would be acceptable to mentally ridicule them. *Are they even trying? Ugh, some people are so lazy.* In this case, it would have been wrong to tell me to try harder, of course. That's just immoral. But I'm sure everyone considered it at some point—they all discretely imagined that awful thought, then shook their heads to cleanse themselves of the filth of it and looked furtively around the room as if to assure themselves that mind reading wasn't possible. But honestly,

I agree with everyone's implicit judgment: It really was a half-hearted attempt.

The Catcher in the Rye, or "Phony"
January 2, 2013

I was Winston. And she was Julia, metaphorically and literally: To my knowledge, it says Julia on her birth certificate. I believed it was "the two of us against the world," when in fact there was no conflict and I had arbitrarily assigned Julia, the person, to Julia, the character, simply for the namesake and the ideal she represented. She could have just as easily been Shakespeare's Juliet for the destructiveness and intensity of our eighth-grade "relationship," Easton-Ellis's Evelyn for the inconsideration I gave her, or Murakami's Saeki for our shared insecurities. You can apply my image of her to any author's works that include idealized women—the only exception I can think of is Vladimir Nabokov. (Please excuse the *sous rature* and the poor excuse for a joke.) A more apt metaphor would put me as Holden Caulfield: unreliable, angsty, and arrogant. I assumed she needed protection (because protection is emasculating) and that also, I needed to share my vulnerabilities with her (because insecurity has been romanticized by every author ever), and it spiraled into a system where I would dump all of my insecurities onto her. And eventually we just fought all the time, so I left page 293 from *1984* on her desk and highlighted the sentence that says "Julia; the razor blade." (Though I did prefer kitchen knives.)

Infinite Jest, or "Te Occidere Possunt Sed Te Edere
Non Possunt Nefas Est"
February 1, 2013

Naman, you have a great smile. Maybe they were just surprised
I was there; I guess a lot of people who have the cops called on
them aren't exactly the most calm and controlled. *Naman, I like
your clothes!* Of course, just below the surface I was outraged,
seething at the "friend" I had trusted. At that point, I would've
gladly denounced her to O'Brien in the hallway outside Room
101—no rats necessary. All it took was one ambiguously word-
ed text message ("Don't bother replying; I'm not going to answer") during a fight—though at that time, what conversations
between us weren't fights?—and suddenly, the cops were there
to whisk me away to be "psychologically assessed to make sure
I wasn't a threat to myself or others." *Naman, your glasses have
a really nice color!* And so despite mostly just telling me nice
things about myself, the social workers had "analyzed" that I
was perfectly in control of my emotions—however, I was still
recommended to see a psychiatrist for whatever reason.

A week later, in the psychiatrist's waiting room, I stared
at the "crazies" around me, wondering whether I was one of
"them" or not. I judged each of their actions in the waiting
room—an eight-year-old playing a Game Boy of sorts, a professionally dressed woman reading one of the copies of *Fitness*
magazine (*Banish Cellulite for Good!*) and another teenager av-
idly texting and avoiding eye contact with me. Aside from the
psychology jokes on the wall (*A Freudian slip is when you say
one thing, but mean your mother!*), it felt just like any other general practitioner's office: There was a tangible lack of screaming, of violence, of straitjackets. The people in that room acted
as if they didn't have diseases ravaging their minds—they sat

like patients at an oncologist's office, seemingly ignorant and unharmed by the chaos in their bodies.

The psychiatrist spoke to me personally for the better part of an hour, mysteriously lacking the infamous notebook-jotting and the incessant inquiries of *how does that make you feel?* I spoke to him about the whole situation and was given a chance to speak organically about my thoughts on the events and also on life in general. And at the end of our conversation, I awaited my verdict of "anxious," "depressed," "bipolar," "insane." What I got was "perfectionist." It took three psychological evaluations to determine that the combination of Chicago winter, teenage hormones, and (primarily) test anxiety had cocktailed to produce a severe reaction to all typical teenage emotional struggles. I was told to come back if I ever experienced any desire to harm myself again, but other than that, I was actually *okay.* So basically, what I'm trying to say here is that they can call the cops on you, but the legalities of diagnosing you are quite a bit dicier.

Kafka on the Shore, or "The Labyrinth"
May 28, 2013

"Should I kill myself or have a cup of coffee?" I hesitate. Eighth grade nears its end, and with it, a phase of my life. Though the mention of suicide opens a pit in my stomach, I ignore my Tartarus and its demons and consider Albert Camus's proposition—not in the literal sense, as a question to be answered, but instead as valid philosophy that I've come to accept.

Following the psychiatrist's personal recommendation, my parents grounded me from technology to allow me to get away from social media and more tension or pressure from the Internet. While initially I was outraged, this period of time has contributed more to my personal growth than any other period in my life. Without the distractions of Reddit and Facebook, I spent my time immersed in music, athletics, and literature in order to give my life meaning. I learned a fifth instrument and became better at the other four; I became a better fencer. I pored over works by Kafka, by Camus, by Hesse, by Wilde, by Sartre, to learn more about the human condition I almost removed myself from. I placed less emphasis on intellectualism and academics. I learned to form my own thoughts and to evaluate others' without criticizing or ostracizing them. I became friends with people I looked down at before, the Ackleys and Stradlaters of my society.

The original concept of the labyrinth was developed by the Mesopotamians, who prototyped it by ripping out the intestines of animals and using the shapes to predict the future—the labyrinth outside is based on the guts inside. I traversed my labyrinth by recognizing that the external parts of my life and identity were projections of what was inside, and that my emotional condition and internal identity was a projection of what was outside. Like Kafka's physical journey to Shikoku, when I made a meaningful decision to step into the labyrinth outside and to change my external circumstances, I found that I had also stepped into the labyrinth inside and changed my inner personality entirely.

I'm sitting at a café in Paris, taking in the view from Montmartre. "May I have a cup of coffee, with no cream?" I ask the waitress. She returns moments later and says, "I'm sorry, Monsieur. We are all out of cream. Would you like your coffee with no milk instead?"

I wake up craving coffee.

How to Breathe

JACK TIEN-DANA, Grade 11, Age 16. Riverdale Country School, Bronx, NY. Susan Katz, *Educator*

Maybe it was too much.

We had love and shelves full of books and everything else. There were pink-frosted cakes and goodnight presents, big parties at our apartment where my mom would say, "A hundred writers, and they all insist on standing in the kitchen so they don't miss the free food!" And the kids would order ginger ales from the bartender and watch TV with my dad and other men who said they'd had enough with the socializing, like Russell Banks or Dan Rather in a Santa suit. There were field trips to the magazine my father edited and the newspaper my mother wrote for. There was the way my bean plant from school grew taller than our dog; the Broadway musicals with Cokes and Junior Mints at intermission; the sleepovers where my mom made us elaborate midnight buffets and chased us down the hall like a streak of light, brandishing a light saber. Our house was full of candy and flowers. My friends wanted to live with us. She was always laughing.

It was too much.

We were in a hardware store in Connecticut when suddenly, it wasn't. It was Memorial Day weekend, and I was six. I was standing by a wall of hinges, inhaling deep breaths of big bags of dirt that smelled like friendly gasoline, when my mother urgently called us from another aisle. She was sitting low—on a coiled garden hose? a spool of chain link?—doubled over.

"Something's wrong," she said. "We have to go to the hospital."

We rushed to the car, and my mother, still clutching her chest, phoned one of her best friends, a writer who is also a doctor. "No, I'm not having a panic attack," she snapped at him. "You've known me for twenty years—have I ever had a panic attack? I can't feel my fingers or toes. I feel like I've been shot in the back. I'm having a panic attack because something's seriously wrong, and you keep telling me I'm just having a panic attack!" At least she's still making jokes, I remember thinking. Maybe it's not so bad. Please don't let it be bad.

When we got to the hospital and she left the car without saying goodbye to me, I knew it was bad.

Hospitals are not huge fans of small children. The next 24 hours were a period of me being shooed away or talked to in aren't-you-a-big-boy voices, or parked in a room with a television mounted near the ceiling. I watched my first episode of *The Simpsons*. My dad bought me Ding Dongs from a vending machine. I found a four-leaf clover on the hospital lawn and saved it. It would bring good luck. It would bring luck to the people who, yesterday, were the luckiest people in the world.

The next day, the hospital transferred my mom to a New York hospital. My father rode with her in the ambulance, while my aunt, a semi-famous fashion editor and full-fledged diva, drove me home with my uncle and cousin. We were on the West Side Highway when she rear-ended a cab. I was holding a full canister of cheese puffs, which jounced in the air and landed all over me. She flew out of the car to excoriate the cabbie (note: *she* rear-ended *him*) and, during a lull in the ensuing fracas, she stuck her head in my window and hissed at a cheese-dusted me, "Don't tell your mother this happened."

I wished I had found a *five*-leaf clover.

When we arrived in New York, my mom was in the step-down of the ICU, the worst place to be. She was paralyzed from the arms down. The doctors said she had acute transverse myelitis, a fluke disease in which the body attacks its own spinal cord. She was heavily medicated, and I wasn't allowed to see her.

"Tell Mom that I love her," I said to my father. "Also, that Aunt Kate got us into a car accident."

"OK," my dad said. "Why is your hair orange?"

A lot happened in the next few years. My mom learned to walk again, and in three months, was able to move around. High-dose steroids made her gain 40 pounds of fluid in 24 hours, and the sudden inflation made her face collapse. She had five surgeries to reconstruct her face, where they harvested cartilage from her ears and hips and ribs and then cobbled it together to make her face a blurred, clumsy version of the original. She never got back the full use of her hands.

I've kept a personal catalog of these medical facts—a few, I remember myself, others, I overheard or read in my mother's magazine articles. My own memories, filtered through the lens of a six-year-old, have less specificity and flow. I remember my mother, immobile in her hospital bed, wearing a blue-and-white bathrobe, a phone propped on the pillow so she could dictate her newspaper column to a machine at the *Times* like an old-fashioned war correspondent. I remember seeing her beloved grand piano closed, like a casket, and adults whispering annoying, unuseful things like "poor little guy" and "*such a tough time.*" I remember that at every wish opportunity—birthday candles, coins in fountains—I would wish that my mom's hands could work again, until I realized that wishes always stay wishes.

Most of all, I remember that this was when my mother started to teach me how to write. Certainly, writing had always had a palpable presence in our home: When I first proudly read *Hop on Pop* aloud to my parents, they interrupted me with, "Who wrote it? Never ignore the byline." Our grocery lists read: milk, bread, TK number of oranges. After my dad and I watched *Toy Story*, he turned to me with satisfaction and said, "Set-up, conflict, epiphany, resolution, kicker—it had it all" (I assumed Epiphany was the name of the actress who played Bo Peep and vigorously nodded my head in agreement).

But when I entered third grade—and our family had finally achieved a baseline level of normalcy—my mother began her informal course of instruction. After school, I would pull up a chair next to her desk, and as she worked, she kept up a running commentary. "Writing needs to breathe," she would say. "Learn to add little breaths to your sentences to create flow. Instead of, *I went to the store today*, you could say, *Today, I went to the store*, or, *I went, today, to the store*. Ask yourself: Where do I need the breath? What creates the best rhythm?"

Or, "Don't use a fifty-cent word if a ten-cent word will do the job," she'd say. "Unless you're Jonathan Swift, vast beats brobdingnagian, any day. Good writing should make the reader think, *That's so true*; choose words because they're true, not because they're fancy. That's why you want to expand your vocabulary—it gives you more options. Writing is all about making choices."

To be sure (breath), it took me a while to absorb (digest? process?) her numerous dos and don'ts: Don't bury your lede but do bury transition words like *however*; never fear long sentences or short paragraphs; be specific, because little details can evoke large feeling; recognize the difference between effective and sloppy repetition; and for the love of God, stop using so many adjectives.

It wasn't until recently, however (aptly buried), that I understood the power of a writer's right to choose. As I watched my mother write articles about her experiences and my father edit them, I realized that when you write about life, no matter how harrowing or unpredictable it may be, you own it. I discovered that even if you can't change reality, you *can* control its rhythm, its scope—in short, where to put the breaths. That, and the fact that Annie Potts was the voice of Bo Peep.

I've written about many things, never about the worst one. Eight years after one terrible fact, though, I'm ready to take control. The screech of brakes, a flickering television in a blue waiting room, a pressed four-leaf clover, the sense that I was too small and this was too big—they've always been there, steady specters, waiting for me. They'll always be there. But now, I choose them. They're mine.

Feathers

ALEXANDER NGUYEN, Grade 12, Age 18. Klein Forest High School, Houston, TX. Royce Gregory Jr., *Educator*

Feathers are strange things to rest your thoughts upon. Spiny leaves of hairy quills, packed to an abundance, a singular insignificance. I could feel the weight of my hand pressing against my ear from the other side in an attempt to regain sensation. Commercial duck feathers. The walls.

—too thin.

The noise seemed to reverberate through the plaster scarred with stabs of thumbtacks from childhood posters. Where I no longer listened to the noise, where instead the sounds seemed to drum on my skin and echo in my ribcage. There is a high and a low sound, sometimes I can tell them apart, sometimes there's just a mass of static. Tonight's dissonance was violent, as it oscillates between Vietnamese and broken English, both laden with accents so thick words were drowned in harsh tones. Vietnamese with a southern drawl. English with an immigrant's ornamentation. Vernacular almost destined for a low-budget Indie film.

My legs outstretched, searching for the cool of the corner just as the door alarm chirped twice. Subtle, quaint, as nonchalant and casual as clinking silverware at a dinner party, it was not a sufficient forewarning to the monumental door slam that followed so abruptly. Some sounds you feel more than you hear. This wasn't the first time. I should have been prepared by now. I never am.

Then ensued the usual tune of male aggressive anger, the purposeless shatter of her favorite porcelain bowls on the cheap vinyl floor. The splintering of heavy oak chairs crashing hard on one another. The collapse of metal blinds. An orchestra of entropy.

It's funny really. When it comes to detecting any news, I am as backwards as a Cold War Soviet Union. Ignorance through self-inflicted isolation. A kind of peace that is without substance, a lack of happening from the nature of emptiness. But sometimes you understand by hearing all of it, not listening. The prosody of white noise that screams the eminent end. The marriage had been failing. Everybody knew. But the sounds tonight acknowledged that reality. The final audible breath of childhood that was so effortlessly uttered. All of a sudden I had realized this, but they hadn't yet.

They saw it as a continuum. They believed that culture and traditions could bear the burden of their differences. As if the film that looped their lives never wore to a breaking point. Instead, they were falling all along, but didn't know it until they hit the ground. They would give it two or three more months and a few days broken off spare weeks before they would realize that it had been over since tonight.

Now that I think about it, it was a shame really. All those feathers, each wisp so fragile but packed so tightly, piled to a solid mass that could have never cushioned a fall.

The sheets twisted around my ankle as I turned to the ceiling. I could hear my heart. Commercial duck feathers. The walls.

—too thin.

Let Light In

JO DE WAAL, Grade 10, Age 15. Greenwich Academy, Greenwich, CT. Jeff Schwartz, *Educator*. Gedenk Award for Tolerance

The glint off the stained-glass panel flashed like flint scratched to stone. It was eight o'clock in the morning and Dutch summer sun had lifted over the Ijsselmeer, drenching the sky delft blue. My dad and I stood on the sidewalk in a sleepy suburb of Amsterdam eyeing a squat red-brick house with a slanting tile roof. I reached for his hand, but he stepped ahead of me onto the tidy lawn. Pressing his cane into damp fescue, he marched up to the house, intent on peeking in the windows of his childhood home. He hadn't lived at the Meentweg street address in over 68 years, but he was determined to show me the pitched attic he had hidden in during the "Hunger Winter" of 1944. I obediently followed him up the slope of the yard. Leaning against the boxwood hedge wrapping around the home, my dad cupped his right hand to the kitchen window. A trickle of sweat ran down my spine, and it wasn't because of the lemon drop sun rising in the sky. We were trespassing, and my dad had no intention of leaving. He stood firm as a time traveler with a mission to mine the past.

"This is the one," he said.

He swung his cane up like a conductor's baton and jabbed it higher.

Morning sunlight streamed through the clear wide window. Brilliant rays illuminated the rose pastel-colored panel—the size of a small desk—crowning the transparent window from above. Etched in curling script, the radiant panel broadcast a sentence written in Old Dutch.

"The writing is a moral story by the sixteenth-century Dutch poet Jacob Cats," said my dad. "I read it many times as a child sitting at a small table in the living room behind this glass." He tapped the window again.

Standing in the dew-soaked hydrangea hedge, my dad shifted his weight to find balance, and then he used his cane as a pointer to read the text aloud. Bright sunlight sparked the script and sprinkles of yellow and pink light peppered the hedge below.

His chapped lips curled around his crooked teeth as he spoke in Old Dutch, its cadence unfamiliar to my twenty-first-century ears.

"Geen nutter ding voor gramme zinnen is stilt te zijn en tijd te winnen," he read. "I'll translate roughly into English: There is no better thing for angry minds than to be quiet and gain time." He stepped out of the bushes, the hem of his trousers soaked with garden moisture. "Life sometimes seems unfair because it is," he said. "But when you're angry, like the saying by Cats, it's better to be patient and find balance so you can think clearly later."

I stood immobile. I was often impatient and wanted immediate change. Sometimes I became angry and wanted easy, fast solutions.

The sun crept higher and hit a crescendo over the tall elms bordering the garden. A woodsy aroma of cedar mixed with soft, rich earth chased through the clean air. My shoulders tightened, and I was ready to leave. I secretly did not want to hear the rest of his story. This was the home in which my dad was captured at gunpoint during the Second World War and marched away to a Nazi-controlled concentration camp. Being here made me queasy for trespassing in the present but also made me want to wretch for trespassing in the past.

"Right here," he said, pointing his cane at the same bay window, "in this room, we jumped into the window benches when the German guards burst in."

I bit the inside of my lip. I knew it had been an early Tuesday morning in September of 1944 when my dad's older sister spotted armed German guards surrounding the house, creeping behind the apple trees. I shivered in spite of the warm sun. I was standing within Frisbee-throwing distance to the same trees.

On that fateful morning, Nazi guards had stormed the home to round up my dad and his two brothers. About a dozen other young men, including my dad's field hockey teammates and neighbors, were held at gunpoint in the middle of the Meentweg street in front of my dad's house. I wanted my dad to stop his story, as if holding back the words would make the horror of what happened disappear.

"My older brother ran upstairs, but my other brother and I scrambled into the window bench to hide," he said. "Piled inside the bench, it was completely dark, and all I heard was the 'tick-tack, tick-tack' of the guard's steel-toed boots on the wood floor."

Even though I knew the story, standing there caused my pulse to pound. My ears started ringing. Sweat ran down my spine as my stomach churned fetid bile.

"Then the footsteps stopped. In the same instant, my brother poked his finger up and lifted the top of the window bench an inch to take a peek. The next thing I knew, the end of the Russian-issued AK47 Karabiner rifle jammed into my ribs," he said. At gunpoint my dad and his brother were forced out of their family home into the unknown.

"There," he said. "My brother and I hid there."

He jabbed his cane upward to the attic. My dad had intentionally fast-forwarded the story. That was his way of dealing with the past he didn't want to talk about. He left out the part of his days in the prison camp. He didn't embellish his escape from the gruesome Nazi camp when he was only six years older than I am. By risking point-blank execution, he took a chance during work detail along the Lower Rhine River and slipped into the abandoned Dutch city of Arnhem in his torn prison rags. With the help of strangers, he foraged in the forest. Weeks later, with the help of the Red Cross, he dressed as a girl and walked fifty miles with a group of women back home. As a fugitive he was forced to hide in the frigid attic, the triangle space looming above us, during one of the coldest winters on record in Holland during November of 1944.

"Words do nothing to explain the dark parts," he said. "It's better I show you the light."

I squinted against the bright sun. The shiny copper downspouts on the house reached up to the roofline and led to the edge of a chimney that ran as high as the elms bordering the yard. A black-and-white magpie drifted into view, then landed on the orange-tiled roof.

"There was no heat," he said. "Once a week, when my dad built a fire in the hearth below, the smoke of green wood seeped through the chimney bricks into the attic. But we did calisthenics up there to keep warm," he said. "And I secretly snuck out during the evening four times a week to my Orange

Brigade resistance meetings. Our group got our instructions from the Dutch government in exile. We helped Canadian and American Allies navigate their way into this section of Holland. I wanted to be part of something bigger than myself. It made me feel useful, like I mattered."

Before I visited his home, I didn't fully understand my dad's stories about unjust imprisonment. Each day, my dad made the day matter. As German occupation tightened the military grip in Holland during December 1944 and into the new year of 1945, food, fuel, and electricity lines remained severed. Subsisting on one cup of thin dried pea soup a day, my dad and his brother stayed sequestered in the dark, subzero attic, and his family gathered around the kitchen table in cold, waning light. In spite of deprivation, the family fostered an ample supply of hope.

Seeing his childhood home opened my eyes. Its simple structure and unassuming façade served as a lens to focus on the courage ordinary people possessed. By seeing his home up close, I began to unravel my complicated preconceptions about war and inch toward understanding my father's experience. By seeing his home, I began to embrace rather than question his wartime ordeal.

My dad's determination to visit his childhood home with me in tow made his home approachable, a forgiving and hopeful place. I inched intellectually closer to understanding his spirit and the spirit of people facing freedom taken away. As a result, I have gained an understanding not only of his life but an awareness of individual will to triumph in the face of adversity.

In the warm summer sun, my dad and I inched across the slate patio.

"Look up there," he said.

I turned and looked.

"See the space, the space between the roof line and the house?" he said.

The dark rectangle of space the size of a shoebox turned on its side ran around the perimeter of the attic.

"Yes, I see it," I said.

"During that winter, we stuffed old kitchen rags in there. To keep the wind out."

"Why didn't you close up the space better?" I asked.

Balancing on his cane he watched a magpie take flight from the roof. The serrated white wings edged in black cut elegant circles above the pitched attic before taking flight higher into the clear sky.

"To let the light in," he said.

I currently live in the United States with my American mother and my Dutch father. Yet in the summer when I visit the Netherlands and I ride my bike with my Canadian, Polish, Dutch, and Ethiopian friends to the beach on the elbow of the Ijsselmeer, I take time to pass my dad's childhood home. Tall elms reaching to blue sky surround the red-brick home holding memories. When I cycle past, I dig my pedals harder and hold my head prouder because I come from a stock of people who see the world not in terms of giving in to dark despair, but rather summoning the will to let light in.

Visit **www.artandwriting.org/galleries** to read this piece in its entirety.

CHAEHONG LEE, *Are These Edible*, Grade 12, Age 17. Newport High School, Newport, WA. Joel Korynta, *Educator*. American Visions Award

When Forever Ends: A Vignette Collection

ARRYN OWENS, Grade 8, Age 14. Lakeside Middle School, Seattle, WA. Susie Mortensen, *Educator*

Mango Popsicle

Elbows crack, rubbery legs curl into metal armrest. Engine roars, ears pop, eyes blurry in midnight darkness. Water slides down raw, cold throat. The ocean far below purrs, wild in gray salt. The plane lands and China is beneath us, muffling our sticky eyes, our sticky clothes, our sticky hands.

The smell. Salty octopus kebab seared in a roadside stall, vinegar breath hot against your cheeks. Smog and sugared bean bread, green bean popsicles and yellow silt. Prying eyes and eager ears and rapid lips and sleek dark hair, they surround us. Here they are, she says. What a journey, he says. You made it, they all say. I only think how far away home is, how far away. Peanut butter and pasta and cheese and grapes. Trees and forks and beer in bottles.

This is home for some people. These streets of steaming mud and bones and slimy dumplings slipping, shoes and spit and elbows, yellow silt, yellow sea. Sticky eyes. Xièxie, zài jiàn. The words twist and slur in my mouth made of glue. Jiànzi, xièxie. Xièxie. Gristly sea cucumber speared by a chopstick, boiled peanuts, pale duck egg blue in its shell. The table spins, dizzy stomach growling at the mystery. What world have these people come from?

Xièxie. Nèi hào. Zài jiàn. Sweat beads on brows as the bus jerks, mango popsicle slippery in calm frost, the only thing that tastes anything like home.

They say there used to be sharks, swimming in the yellow bay. So they made a net. Made a net, they say. Yes. They say it's been years and years and no one knows if the sharks still swim. But we keep it there just in case, they say. Yes, and nod. So we swim in the yellow silt, the yellow sea, which used to have sharks. Mist and sticky eyes, sand grinding between toes.

Nèi hào, jiànzi, zài jiàn. Pagoda shrouded in mist, a tree with four lives. Monks frown at the hesitant camera. You take picture? Their eyes ask. Why picture of us? You are the real attraction, and they turn away.

Water slides against raw, cold throat. Engine roars, ears pop, elbows crack. Rubber legs and sticky eyes. And then we are home. I have never been happier to see peanut butter, pasta, and cheese and grapes. Grapes, bananas, apples. Brown sand, blue sea. Zài jiàn. Goodbye, yellow silt, octopus kebabs, sleek hair of silk, boiled peanuts. Goodbye, China.

The Dog With Fur of Ashes

In that space between day and night, when light hunches, plodding into the distance, and darkness swoops like the flapping of frantic bats, Heidi's mom wanders. A wisp of a woman, blending more into the air than anything else, I bet she could drift along her winding path each day for a decade—a lifetime—and never be seen, never be noticed. But I did. I noticed.

Dubious, curious, watching in stricken silence, my eyes flick between her and the kitchen table, a window and an infinity between us. That hunched dog sauntering behind, with a mangy coat of ash and shadows, with a downturned muzzle and bony hips poking as if to steal all your sympathies. The follower. His tail sags in discord, in gloom, like he'd have a million, million things to say if he'd ever get up the courage to break their silence. In discord, in despair, because he knows he never will.

A window and an infinity between us, I wonder. Wonder what tragedies hang between them—a dog lost in impossibility and a woman lost in reality. Wonder what she ever had against him, a dog with a downturned muzzle, wanting nothing in the world but to be loved. Wonder how much they have forgotten and how much they can never forget.

There, then gone. Through the maze of swaying pines that scold the fence posts and trellis vines, through the flippant creek and squirrels skittering their worries away, through the wilting dandelions bent in waiting. There, then gone. Alone in each other's company, it seems the only reason he ever followed her is because he'd have no other place to go, that dog. Because he'd have nothing left but poking hips and fur of ashes and a million years of silence. Instead he gets poking hips, fur of ashes, a million years of silence, and someone to walk behind.

Heidi. An explosion of a girl, she always seemed to be cartwheeling more than not cartwheeling. Maybe that's why she's so short and round—all that centripetal force wadding up everything worth anything.

You know, I think I named her Heidi's mom because I wanted to dream her something better than what she's got, because when the lines around your mouth tell your stories for you, you deserve something more than a reality you never wanted and a dog to walk ahead of. You know?

All because of Heidi's mom, plodding in the crease of nothing, her dog of ashes that tells her stories for her, and me, who noticed. You know, maybe in this world we all need a Heidi. A way out. Heidi, for the sake of those lost in themselves, for everyone who drifts in silence, chasing their fantasies and blending into the air. You know?

Hands Like Soot and Time

Every year on our way down South, we stop at Grandma and Papa's. That house, with the thin-stemmed chrysanthemums reaching for your hand, with the mulch pile in the backyard corner and the spongy teal carpet dancing before your eyes like marimbas. Like Sprite with ice and movies in bed, the carpet that dances like marimbas. Sacramento. That's where. The word is too difficult for my young tongue. Scrackamento? Samcramento. That's it. Stracklametro, Sackamarto, Slackamato, until it's just Sack of Tomatoes, because that's easier. Mommy, are we there yet? Are we in Sack of Tomatoes? Soon, honey. Soon.

But the sun, high above my squinting eyes, says we've got miles and miles until that hay bale darkness, miles and miles and miles left to go. So we drive and we drive and my ears and my eyes droop like melting rubber and the time passes slow, slow, slow. Roaring by the rusted grain fields swaying, past the blotchy cows with thick teeth chewing, we roar the road away, that road, straight as a ruler that goes and goes and goes. And since I'm five now and I know everything, I tell everyone that even when forever ends, even after you can't see it anymore, I know this road keeps on going, it just goes and goes and goes and goes. Yep. Thirteen hours, I say—trying to fit all those on my fingers—isn't forever, but it sure feels like it.

Then there's blurred city lights, and the cows aren't chewing with their thick teeth anymore, and they drape me over a shoulder to carry me in, nodding in my drowsiness, carry me in. Inside, a house that smells like chrysanthemums and Papa's shaving cream, the Sunday paper and tomato leaves. Gentle hands tuck the crispy sheets under my chin, whisper, whisper, far away. Then the gentle hands tip-toe out, *Shhh.* Dark shadows and fall asleep to the sound of crickets, the sound of crickets, fading, fading away.

Morning mist, the dripping sun pouring golden ichor through a beaming window, white leather couch and his hands, huge and soft and sturdy, with deep wrinkles like soot and time, like soot and time and long days under the sun. That raisin toast, always that same raisin toast sliced in thick-crusted squares dripping with butter, browned by a drawer-imprisoned steel toaster. And since I am eight now, I can squeeze my own oranges into orange juice, squish back and forth and suck up the sticky extra, slurp!

Chlorine-hardened swimsuits and spray the sunscreen outside please. Water fights and sprinkler games and swimming in Uncle Marty's pool three doors down, just three doors down can we go there now? And why did Uncle Marty buy a house three doors down from Grandma and Papa? Who knows why Uncle Marty does anything, and that's all the answer you're gonna get when I start to ask more. But did you know—you do know, don't you? Everybody knows that there's a monster at the bottom of Uncle Marty's pool. Just make sure you don't tell anyone, because they might get scared. Well, I know there is one because he told me, Uncle Marty told me. He always stays at the deepest of the deepest parts, and if we ever go down there, he'll suck our little toes up just like the algae he eats off the bottom. Just like that! Can you believe it?

But now I'm eleven and the house is sold and gone, the flowers withered, dry and drooping. So we spend our days at the crumbly-silt River, the River I can cross all by myself. Rust-brown silt scratches the skin from shins, snakes slither and hiss into chattering bushes, ham sandwich and Doritos at noon. Watch the minnows scatter as the current yanks the hours away.

And then I'm thirteen, another summer up and gone, yanking the hours away. Who yanked all those hours away? Oh red-rusted, silt-crusted River, don't yank those sweet hours away. Please don't yank those sweet hours away.

Visit **www.artandwriting.org/galleries** to read this piece in its entirety.

NFL'Oréal: A New Kind of Cover-Up

ABIGAIL SWOBODA, Grade 11, Age 17. Kennard-Dale High School, Fawn Grove, PA. Wes Carter, *Educator*

Do you struggle to find quality makeup that really does the trick? Have issues disguising those problem areas on your face and body? Well the solution is now clear: NFL'Oréal! NFL'Oréal is the new groundbreaking makeup brand formed by the National Football League (NFL) and cosmetics brand L'Oréal.

Cosmetic scientists are creating new formulas even as you read this to find the perfect mixture of lies and pigment to fool the eyes of the general public.

And who better to trust for a great cover-up than the NFL?

Foundation and concealer are only two examples of many products that will soon be released to consumers to help them present their own false face to the public. Eye shadow, lipstick, and blush will also be offered by the upcoming brand that is sure to be a real hit with domestic violence survivors in particular.

With a flick of the wrist of NFL'Oréal, it's almost as if those minor punches never even happened!

NFL'Oréal will offer a wide variety of facial makeup shades so that everyone is covered completely, just in case a false rumor were to slip out anywhere.

Former Chicago Bears scout Jerry Angelo said: "We knew [the cover-up of abuse incidents] was wrong . . . For whatever reason, it just kind of got glossed over."

And just as those minor incidents were "glossed over," your lips can be too, with NFL'Oréal's special line of Loophole Lipgloss. The line will include shades like: "No Proof Peach," "Ray Rice Red," and the high-demand shade "We're-Married-So-It-Doesn't-Count Watermelon." In addition to these fun flavors, NFL'Oréal will offer hundreds of other colors that will be released in the future, almost like the "hundreds and hundreds" of domestic violence cases within the NFL that have been so conveniently ignored.

Eyeliner has been the most debated product in the line, as it was quickly taken off the website with NFL'Oréal brand executive Brandon Robertson's only comment being that black rings around the eyes weren't exactly the "look they were trying to achieve."

However, in the absence of eyeliner, the brand will still offer a small grouping of eye shadows all based around the color blue.

If you're looking for green, orange, or any other shade, NFL'Oréal assures that you can just use blue; it's not like anyone would notice anyway. But if your hand does happen to slip a little bit, there's always more cover-up.

Robertson said, "[NFL'Oréal's] goal is to offer high-quality makeup to the masses that reflects the aims of the National Football League: great appearances."

Prices have been placed at around $5,000 to start, which is also the average fine for a Class A misdemeanor or felony charge. But for football players who are interested, the brand will be completely free; they are used to getting off with no charge anyway.

As Robertson also said, "We are looking into finding the perfect models for the brand, but there are no definite choices as of now."

NFL'Oréal is currently seeking models for their advertisements. Notable front-runner is former Baltimore Raven Ray Rice's now wife Janay Rice, selected for her "special knowledge" in the field.

Publicity for the project on the whole has been difficult in terms of presentation, however, considering tension from human rights groups that emerged after the announcement of the brand on January 2nd. NFL'Oréal promises that the issue has been cleared up now, though, as they issued a sincere apology to those who were unfortunately offended for whatever reason.

Whenever the brand does drop, however, be sure to keep your eyes peeled, because with such air-tight coverage, it might be hard to sniff out in the mainstream media. NFL'Oréal: on some shelves now!

Cruel and Unusual Punishment

JORDAN HARPER, Grade 10, Age 15. Alabama School of Fine Arts, Birmingham, AL. Stuart Flynn, *Educator*

Once the world became overpopulated, the eighth amendment was put under loose interpretation. All lawbreakers are now executed via laughter—"unusual but charitable punishment," as President Burnham described it. He thought he was so considerate, letting us spend our final moments on a dopamine high. But I have to admit, we could do worse.

Groups are the best company to go with. They make laughter more probable because the peer pressure helps; no one wants to seem left out of the joke, because no one wants to be alone in death. We are shuffled into a room, appropriately called the Final Destination Room, FDR, and strapped to brain monitors. We will stay there until scientifically altered and highly concentrated nitrous oxide ventilates through slots in the ceiling and kills us. The walls are visible from the other side, where our families will watch us laugh to death. The only adornment in the room, a sign with large, neon-pink letters: NO FEAR HERE! They tell us once our anxiety levels are preferably low, jokes will be told to us over speakers and we will laugh until cardiac arrest or asphyxiation puts us to sleep. My brother next to me looks as though he wants to take a nap. He is always so bored, even at the end. We spent our last few weeks with our family, saying goodbyes, apologizing. "Did you know people used to get their heads cut off in front of the entire town?" He showed me yesterday, looking up past methods of execution, trying to find solace in our situation.

"Put that away!" my mother said from the kitchen. She wept over a pot of broth, trying to prepare our final meal—but I feel it was for show. She was a mess of emotion all week, sad, angry, perhaps happy that the rambunctious behavior of her misfit children had finally brought their lives to an end. I don't think she could decide whether she felt like a failure as a mother or relieved that she would be rid of us. The thought that she could enjoy this made the end a lot easier to face.

A voice comes over the speaker.

"Hello, Lori Applebaum, Reba Applebaum, Stanley Evans, Jennifer Traewek, Megan Zhu, and Michale Zhu. I am your Speech Interpretation and Recognition Interface, but you can call me SIRI."

I can tell SIRI really wants to be my best friend. Its voice is guileless, genderless, save for a vague femininity, which I think adds to the "you should be comfortable" factor. Men always scared me. They always expected something from you, a kiss on the cheek, a hug, a handjob. SIRI tells me no lies. It pronounces my brother's name "Mike-Hail." It wants to push me out of this world with one last, sinless companion. There is to be no fear here.

"You are all here to be terminated for your crimes against humanity. While it is our preference that everyone may live peacefully, felons are a flaw in the system and must be eradicated. Before you end, let us begin! Let's start off by selecting your personal paradises. Lori and Reba Applebaum, please choose one of the following settings: sunset on the beach, snowy mountain peak, tranquil forest, open fields, city skyline, under the sea, or across the universe."

Across from me are another pair of twins, Siamese, two heads on one body. The girls whisper to each other, occasionally giggling, and I wonder if they are gossiping about how SIRI's scenery options sound like cheap fragrances. I envy them. I wish I could speak with my brother so privately one last time. The one on the right says, "Up my ass, please." Her sister hollers; I predict they'll be the first to go. I can't imagine sharing a set of lungs will work to their advantage in our situation.

"I'm sorry, could you repeat that?" SIRI says, politely. It's only doing its job, it does not deserve this ridicule.

"I'm sorry, up *your* ass." Lori and Reba high-five each other—well, clap. They think they are so clever, rejecting their fate like this. I think I'll laugh especially hard once their heads fall onto their shoulders.

"If you're indecisive, I can choose for you. Will snowy mountain peak make you most comfortable?"

They both raspberry.

"You have selected snowy mountain peak." A small television is lowered in front of the twins. "Stan*ley* E*vans*, please choose from the following paradises . . ."

On my right is a quiet, elderly man. I try to read him. His face is stoic and emotionless, whether because he does not want to cry in front of us or because he is determined not to let this gas kill him, I cannot decide.

"Hi, I'm Megan," I whisper and try to turn my hand toward him, a stunted attempt at a handshake. He does not look at me and inhales deeply. I let my hand fall against the restraints—good last impressions are so hard to make.

"If you are indecisive, I can choose for you. Will city skyline make you most comfortable?" He confirms this option with silence and another screen is lowered. I feel like he's glad to focus on something else.

Across from me is a very thin woman, and I wonder if she even had a last meal. She is the only one in the room pleading. When SIRI asks for her to select a paradise, she only pleads. "Please don't kill me! I have children! Please!" A pulsating bubble of snot under her nose married with the blotchy redness of her face makes her head look like an angry pimple ready to pop. Ironically enough, married with actual drops of water on her face is a collection of teardrop tattoos that help me guess why she may be here. Does she really have children? How many have they killed? Do any of those drops represent them? She seems older than Stanley and the only miserable-looking person in the room. I assume this is because she is old enough to remember a time where generations were not so desensitized to death and never grew up with such a twisted view of the value of life; maybe murder was her way of trying to connect with her grandkids. I feel bad for her and hope she gets to laugh the hardest.

"Shut up," my brother says to her, unsympathetic. "They don't care about you or your kids. You're going to die today."

"Michale!" I try to slap him on the wrist but remember I cannot reach him—I will never be able to touch him again. "Be considerate! You act like you don't care any more than they do!" I face her. "Don't worry. It will be like watching your favorite sitcom. It won't feel bad at all." She looks as though she doesn't believe me but lets her head fall back against the chair.

Jennifer seems to be the only person in the room willing to talk to me like a normal person at the moment. She looks like she could use a friend. "Why don't you let SIRI calm you down? Just ask for a scene, anything that'll get you settled."

SIRI asks again for a scene. After some incomprehensible

uttering, SIRI offers to decide for her and Jennifer rejects. "Snowy mountain peak, I guess."

That's when the voice asks me to pick. I am proud to be the first person in the room to answer seriously and without hesitation, and SIRI's screen lowered before me depicts deep space. Naturally, my brother lashes out a long string of curses at SIRI and it gives him sunset on the beach. I wonder why he can never just cooperate, when a sickly sweet taste settles on my tongue.

They've started the gas.

"I'm so sorry," my brother tells me, but he is smiling. His voice is warbled and echoes, like he is speaking to me underwater. The sound makes my lips stretch open in a wide, toothy grin, and I feel like a doll having their smile sewn into them, immortalizing a contented expression.

"Hey, I've got a joke for you," says Stanley, the gas finally loosening him up. "How many cops does it take to fix a light bulb?" We shrug. "They won't fix it. They'll arrest the bulb for being broke and beat the room for being dark." He chortles heartily and we are all laughing, we all get it.

The speaker crackles and I'm glad the old man got to beat them with the first joke. SIRI recites our death sentence.

"What musical is about a train conductor?"

There is a short pause for anticipation, for us all to guess and wonder "What?! What musical?!" then:

"My Fare, Lady."

Our amusement sounds like thunder. I can hear every reaction their bodies make at the hilarity, the twins' chest heaving, the old man's vocal chords vibrating. Jennifer's tears splashing on the ground, my own brother's convulsions of mirth. I think this is the happiest any of us have been in our entire lives.

"Two peanuts walk into a bar."

What did they order, what did they talk about?

"One was a salted."

This kills Stanley. In the middle of his laugh, he seizes. I watch his gnarled, aged fingers try to claw out of the leather straps as he begins gasping for air. I want to worry for him, but the next joke rolls through (What did the coach say to his losing team of snakes? You can't venom all!), and I guffaw when his head falls over as though the top of his spinal column was broken, a phantom smile still etched upon his purple face.

"Oh my God!" Jennifer has to have the world record for most tears on one person's face, sadness, laughter, and the inky signature of her victims all playing together on her cheeks as though they were best friends who were meant to be with each other. She screams about her chest hurting, and I'm surprised by how painless it is to watch as she begs for help but no one can do anything. No one wants to. She finally dies after an hour or so of going on like this. I think of her victims; what will they do with her in the after-life? I imagine them circled around her, like a vengeful gang. "Well, well, well, look who we have here!"

Michale dies immediately after her. When SIRI tells us something about a pessimist, an atheist, and a scientist, I think he becomes overwhelmed, and I hear his ribs crack along with a desperate wheeze and he slumps over. I call his name to him over and over again because I don't want him to miss the next joke. "Michale! Not yet, this one's a real killer!" *Womb to the tomb.* I've always promised my brother this before a crime but never thought it would be so literal. I think I want to mourn him, but then it occurs to me that I can never be sad again.

My prediction is proved very wrong when the Applebaum siblings and I are the only ones left. I have never been good at predictions. My miscalculations were what got me and my brother caught after our last bank heist. "You idiot!" he called me, all guns on us. My hands were in the air like the yellow forky thing on each end of a football field, and I was ready to receive the bullets. 3-0, Megan Zhu!

I suddenly hear Lori (Reba?) scream in delight. "Oh God! I can't hear her!" and soon after there is a rasping breath. Then silence.

I am alone in the universe. I look at my own little screen of darkness and galaxies and wonder where my cell mates are among them. I choose the spiral furthest to the left and focus on it, imagining all of my very last friends welcoming me with open arms. I wonder what the first joke I'll tell them in heaven will be. "Did you hear the one about the inbred boy and the post office worker?"

I never take my eyes off my future corner of the universe as I lose my ability to inhale. I hope my brother is nicer there. I hope Lori and Reba are more mature. I hope Stanley is more vocal, and I hope Jennifer finally understands why her grand-children laugh at horror movies. These wishes bring light to the darkness beginning to ring around my eyes, robbing me of my peripheral vision, like I'm seeing through a narrow tube. I think of my mother's glaucoma and imagine it is the last thing she passes on to me before we part forever. She does like me!

SIRI offers one last nugget of wisdom: "What do you call a non-prophet organization? Atheism."

Nothing Is the Best Punishment

NOAH MAINS, Grade 11, Age 16. Carroll High School, Fort Wayne, IN.
Seth Slater, *Educator*

There's a glitch in Chicago's West Side, a tall proud building that doesn't belong. It's nested between single-story flats and shuttered smoke shops. A beautiful building, it is, with gilt-edged doors and obsidian-black glass running up its side. They named it the Guardia Rehabilitation Center, and it's a sharp departure from the squat, sprawling barbed-wire affairs that dominate prison architecture and have done so for the past three centuries. To the casual observer, it resembles more the Waldorf Astoria than Alcatraz.

As the gate opened, Keynes took his ticket back from the kiosk and pulled into the parking lot. Before he left, he took special care to secure his squad car, double-checking both the lock and the alarm. Two officers were on review because their duty shotguns were stolen from unlocked cruisers, and Keynes didn't feel like he should be the third.

Guardia was a travesty, if one were to see things through Keynes's eyes. He wasn't a stick-in-the-mud nostalgic, and yet the idea of pampering society's outcasts didn't sit well with him. It was an offense, and even more repugnant after he'd seen the freshly dug grave of a friend of his—another police officer, one who'd made a mistake in the line of duty. Unfortunately, his superiors hated it as well, and so Keynes was given an assignment he hated: He was to volunteer for Guardia as an assistant. The man he was assigned to assist, said his memorandum, was one John L. Kingman, Ph.D.

Kingman was a bit of an enigma. Keynes had heard the name before, because the man was rightly famous for his doctorate analyses of prison riots. If the rumors were to be believed, Guardia was almost entirely his pet project. The man had a messianic reputation, and he had held the District Attorney's attention for some time now. It was conceivable, given Kingman's fame, that Guardia was a one-man show.

"Don't judge the system, Keynes. You've only seen it on paper. Wait until you get a look at the finished product," said Kingman, setting his feet atop a bar stool.

"I didn't say anything, sir."

"You've been judging Guardia, and me too, I guess. I know I'm not all that impressive in person; I don't need to be reminded of that. But Guardia can hold its own." Kingman didn't mention how he gained these insights, but it wasn't magic. Keynes's last psychological evaluations, barely a month old, were in a file cabinet to the right.

"I don't mind if you second-guess me," Kingman continued, "because that keeps me on my toes, but at the same time I don't want to hear pointless moaning about my project." Keynes smelled blood and was all too quick to move in for the kill.

"Then you admit that it's your personal project? It's for your idle curiosity, isn't it, and not so much for the punishment of real criminals?"

"I misspoke. It's not my pet project," Kingman shamelessly lied, "but it is, yes, an experiment. Like every other law professional, I want to see the most efficient form of justice." Keynes believed himself to be a professional, whether he agreed with the psychologist or not. To say that out loud, though, would be immature. Rather, he started the conversation again.

"I'm sorry. When do they get here?"

When the prison bus arrived at the Guardia Center for Criminal Rehabilitation, the passengers were told that it was a maximum-security installation, though it wasn't the sort of maximum security that a sane man would envision. The arriving crowd in its entirety was staring in bewilderment, and so Frank Greenberg did as well. No matter the circumstances, it was paramount not to be the tallest blade of grass, the one that gets cut down first. Frank Greenberg was the richest man in the group, despite his scrubby hair and eyes that always seemed to squint. He was a criminal for sure—a bank robber—and he was very good at what he did. Like most children, he'd been told that crime didn't pay, and he was pleasantly surprised when, in fact, it did. The interest on that payment, Greenberg's questionable fortune, was laundered well through a Bahamian bank. And that quantity of interest alone made him worth a low seven figures. As might be assumed from his success, Greenberg was a criminal, but not a dolt.

Guardia's atrium was opulent. Although there were possibly other words for the insane expense of its open lobby, "opulent" was the most accurate. There were bars across the windows and nowhere else. Quietly, Greenberg praised the theories of modern psychologists. He'd take a luxurious "rehabilitation" over punishment any day. Perhaps he'd dodged the executioner's syringe for now, and that was a wonderful thing to turn over in his head. Like any logical man, he assumed that there'd be a catch, but soon he had to admit that there wasn't one. Or, perhaps, it was hidden very well.

The guards didn't look like guards either. Greenberg felt more comfortable referring to them as stewardesses and bellhops, and so he did. In fact, he did so out loud. They didn't seem to mind. One of the more personable "stewardesses" took him and several others up to the sixth floor in an open glass elevator. It was a strange contrast, he thought, between the woman's business suit and skirt (he could also see the faintest outline of a handgun held against her ribs) and the orange pajamas that had served for four years as his prison uniform. The expansive atrium windows showed a view of the entire city, but they were barred by reinforced metal grates. What a strange little world, but it seemed to be several steps up from solitary confinement, and so he relished it.

Keynes and Kingman both were watching the elevator's progress on a television monitor—No. 72—that was one of a multitude covering the top floor's west wall. Kingman pointed at Greenberg, a little figure with an unkempt brown mustache, whose eyes were shifting around the elevator and never stopping. "Do you see that man, the one in the center? He looks intelligent." *He'll be the first to go*, Kingman predicted, wagering a bottle of whisky to himself.

"What's special about that fellow? Does it really matter?"

"Most people would concentrate on the luxuries: They'd be staring at the crystal chandeliers or the bar, which I've been told is well-stocked, incidentally. We might sneak a visit later, if you'd like. Mustache Man, well, he's looking at the window grate, and at the cut of the guard's suit. He's probably noticed that she is armed."

"Should we be overly worried?"

"Of course not. Unless he makes his move right now—and he won't—he'll very quickly get used to luxury."

Greenberg was shown his room by the lady guard. Inside was a pleasant panoramic view of the city's south side. It had a single restroom, a single bed, and a single desk with a single lamp atop it. There was a mini-bar and a room service menu as well, to satisfy his primal needs in an elegant way; Maslow would be proud. In addition, there were several sets of casual and formal clothing in the closet, tailored nicely but not to his size. In any case, the orange jumpsuit was a thing of the past. Everything was brand new, the bed was soft and clean, and as he read through the literature, he realized that the menu was extensive. For the second time that day, he wondered what the catch was. For the second time that day, he had to admit that there didn't seem to be one. Even the guards, armed though they were, were polite.

A week went on without confrontation or conflict. Greenberg noticed that he'd gained some weight around the middle, a consequence of too many sundaes and too much shrimp. That was fine; he was gaunt before. If he became any heavier, he'd ask the guards at the front desk for a bathroom scale. They really were accommodating, the guards. If they could save you effort in any way, they would. Greenberg wondered exactly how hard it would be to train the pigs as hospitality staff, and after he had thought about it, was glad that it wasn't his job. Apparently there was only one rule: no two "prisoners," in the loosest sense of the word, were allowed in the same apartment at any one time. The building enforced that mandate itself, to Greenberg's surprise.

Greenberg had met a young woman in the bar, with close-cropped brown hair and a congenial smile. Her name was Tracy, and she'd been arrested for $2 million of Medicare fraud. Compared to the rapists and occasional murderer he'd met, she seemed like an entirely decent sort of person. When he took her to his room, the sliding door wouldn't open to his fingerprint. It remained closed until she was about twenty-five feet away, then it unlocked without question. No matter how Greenberg schemed to smuggle her in, the door would close before she could enter. Out of sheer perversity, he placed a metal trashcan over the threshold to see if it'd stop the door. It didn't; the bucket was shorn in half by the door's swift pneumatics. A few minutes later, a riot-suit came off the maintenance elevator and delivered a swift, stern reprimand for the destruction of property, really just a slap on the wrist. That was all. Since then, he hadn't tried blocking the door again.

There were a great deal of other things to do. For a while, he practiced pool in the game room, but quickly became good enough that none of the other inmates were willing to play him. Even the bar started to lose its appeal when it turned out that the people there were more interested in drinking than talking. That evening he spent in a soft recliner, bouncing a ping-pong ball off the wall and catching it in an empty margarita glass, over and over again, with just a little mournfulness. He didn't know why, because he'd always liked being by himself. It felt like a real punishment when it happened here.

"I don't get it," insisted Keynes. "How on earth did the Senate approve this? It's got to be painfully hard on the coffers."

"Not really," replied Kingman, as he set down a stained "Best Grandpa Ever" mug—one of three in his drawer. "There's not nearly as much spent on security here as in other prisons, even if the room-and-board cost is higher. Factor in that each prisoner spends a maximum of six or seven months here, and it looks splendidly cheap both on paper and in the real world."

"Each prisoner spends only six months here?" Keynes quoted, with a little doubtful superiority slinking into his voice.

Kingman didn't answer the implied question. He turned back to his coffee.

The next morning Greenberg felt horrible. It wasn't the margarita, because he would've known if it was. For a little while he considered another shot at Tracy, but he changed his mind as soon as he was out of his room. Some famous guy, probably Aristotle, had once said that the definition of insanity is expecting a different result from the same action. By no means was Greenberg crazy.

There were two conflicting emotions that fought for his attention. The first feeling was anger. Greenberg was angry at himself for living with this indulgence. There was no discussion of escape amongst the others. In fact, almost no one talked anymore, and the cops weren't reviled or even resented. The other emotion was a passive one, perhaps not even an emotion, but just the lack of one, and it was the more insidious of the two. It was complacency, and it devised all sorts of arguments as for why Greenberg should be satisfied. He had been given nearly any luxury he could ask for, and that was a damn sight better than the death row apartment he'd have otherwise. Besides, what else could he do? Getting out would be impossible, he'd decided that weeks ago. There was too much security on the ground floor, and only a madman would try to climb the sheer glass precipice that was the exterior wall. Suicide was the only other reasonable escape, and that, he knew, was the preserve of weaker men.

Officer Keynes had been wanting to ask a question of Kingman for some time now. "Why don't they riot? If they've got nothing left to live for, why do they just sit there like idiots?"

The good doctor smiled a rare, lopsided, toothy smile. "I

was hoping you'd ask that very same question. Certainly it's a better line of inquiry than the constant badgering from morons about cost, safety, and security." He continued speaking, looking contentedly at the wall. "It's simple when you break it down to essentials. There's nothing to riot for."

"What about purpose? You've been systematically depriving their lives of meaning ever since they came here." Keynes had begun to think of the prisoners less as men and more as experiments. This was despite every vow he'd ever taken as a police officer, but he was more than a police officer now. He was a minor functionary of God.

"Purpose isn't a concrete concept. People riot for higher wages, for nicer houses, for freedom of speech, but not for love, happiness, or purpose. There isn't a demagogue who'll get up on his soap box and demand that the authorities give him *purpose*," Kingman snorted.

Greenberg helped himself to a cigarette in the little glass cupola built for smokers. As he took in a breath of tar (it would probably kill him), he wondered what he should do, not just that day, but every day. Perhaps he could be the rebel, but wouldn't that be futile? What was there that he was still in want of? He could riot for the opening of the doors, but in the grand scheme of things, would that be important? Would any others join him if he did? He doubted it. Embezzlers, drinkers, assassins, crackheads, and dealers, they were all infatuated with Guardia's diamonds and caviar. Would they risk it all for one more privilege? Without a doubt, no. No one would ever act because this place was more addictive than anything drug dealers sell. There was nothing left for Frank Greenberg now.

With the snubbed cigarette in hand, he took the elevator to the sixth floor, his floor, with a tuxedoed guard watching him intently. Over the room service's phone, he ordered a soda, then a shot of whiskey, then vodka. The alcohol didn't stop coming, armed bellhops knocking every twenty minutes with another bottle of Stolichnaya on a tray, even though he hadn't phoned for more. When he was stuporous, he pulled off his leather belt and tied it around the ceiling fan. Then he sat down on the bed and thought. Another bottle arrived. When it was finished, he haltingly pulled up a stool beneath the belt and sat on it, watching the room melt before his eyes and waiting for that one last bottle.

At 11:23 pm, the last carafe arrived, the concierge pretending not to notice the makeshift gallows in the room. Greenberg took one swallow that burned his numb throat, wiped his mouth clumsily, and stood up on the stool.

It was as he kicked the stool out that Greenberg had that last-minute flash of insight that's bedeviled the doomed for centuries. He panicked, eyes wide, and that panic might have been part of it, but he also saw the intentions of his captors. They weren't benevolent altruists. The name of the place, the Guardia Rehabilitation Center, that was a lie too. There was no rehabilitation here. But . . . too late now.

"Did you see the look in his eyes? He panicked," growled an unnamed officer in the background, who knew he'd face his own death with more machismo.

"That's not unusual. Suicidals often lose their nerve in the last moments," said Keynes.

Kingman and Keynes, side by side, watched the screen. Greenberg's portly body hung from the ceiling fan, toes still shuddering a little in the room's still air. It was only the first death-by-suicide, and by all signs, it'd not be the last. On the television, a young, strong coroner's deputy entered Greenberg's room from the hall, pronouncing him dead at 11:25 pm. The prisoner's corpse was lifted off the contrived noose, like an old heavy coat from its rack, and laid on a stretcher for interment.

Said the psychologist, "It's like the death penalty, but I feel less guilty about administering it."

Keynes didn't respond. He just clicked off television No. 23 with a little fear, a little reverence, in his eyes.

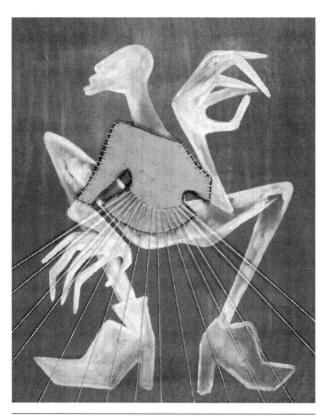

IAN DANNER, *Poise*, Grade 11, Age 16. York Country Day School, York, PA. Stephen March, *Educator*. American Visions Award

Three Reports Concerning the Reaper

JAE HAENG RHEE, Grade 10, Age 16. Trinity Valley School, Fort Worth, TX. Donald Carlson and Lucas Jacob, *Educators*

Report 1, or How a Philosopher Tried to Save Humanity and Brought About an Opposite Result

When confronted by Grim Reaper, Zeno decided to fight for his life.

"Wait," shouted Zeno, when the figure was about to strike his neck. "Before you declare me dead, please explain: When exactly did I cease to be alive? You do realize that it is fairly unclear when my ego came to a halt. When I ceased to breathe? When my heart stopped? When?"

"You died today," Reaper replied, a little confused.

"No. See, skinny fellow. You are not being specific enough. Today when? Now, before you answer by saying the hour or the minute of my end, remember that no matter how specific you become, I can still ask for more details. A day comprises hours, an hour comprises minutes, a minute comprises seconds, and a second comprises still smaller units. This, as is obvious, can go on infinitely. How then will you claim that I died at any certain point of time, when you are utterly unable to pin it down?"

Reaper felt his nonexistent heart sink in his bony chest. If the reasoning was correct, he realized, this was not just about Zeno; it applied to every single human life that existed upon dry lands. He was about to lose his job. Reaper remembered the old days, before the dawn of Humanity, when he had to live in his mom's garage because of his all-time unemployment, and was determined not to let that happen again. He needed a solution.

"Until now, I managed to handle my task by knowing the dates of people's deaths. My unit of measurement is days. Now, this mortal challenges the assumption that this is clear enough information, and claims any given day is infinitely divisible. Infinitely divisible . . ." Then the solution hit Reaper. He turned to Zeno, smiling.

"Instead of cutting you down with just one stroke, I'll simply strike you infinite times during the day. Therefore I say: Today you die."

It did not take Reaper so long to realize that this was quite an arduous task. When he was striking for the 672 tredecillion 489 duodecillion 542 undecillion 552 decillion 755 nonillion 995 octillion 955 septillion 555 sextillion 678 billion 759 million and 486 thousandth time, Reaper had to admit he couldn't get the job done alone. It was a lot of work, and for the sake of fairness, the same thing had to be done to everyone on his destined day. There were more than 7 billion people on the planet, and Reaper needed to hire assistants.

"Like, a lot of them," he thought.

Since there was literally an infinite number of tasks, Reaper had to continue hiring new reapers. No number of them seemed enough, and there seemed to be no end. When he realized he had used up all the potentially employable adults and children above age sixteen, and after he had quelled two deadly revolts by suburban mothers protesting the fact that so many able young men were working for so grim a task, Reaper began outsourcing the jobs to foreign countries whose diligent citizens did not mind working without corporate insurance or being skeletal like proper reapers. After he hired the last person in the entire Underworld who was not yet a deliverer of death, Reaper, still unsatisfied, decided to use robots. He built multiple generators that ceaselessly spit out mechanical reapers, and when they started doing their task, he built still bigger generators that constructed the generators that generated the mechanical reapers. In this way he could accelerate the rate at which the reapers increased. Then he began working on generators that generated the generators that generated the generators that generated the robots, and after he turned them on and saw them working, kept building still grander generators, mad with passion and excitement at the awesome sight of what he had achieved.

Even today, eons after the heroic challenge of an overly cerebral Greek at the face of Death, the number of reapers continues to increase at an ever-increasing speed. This is the story of the origin of those incalculable angels of death who are underpaid and forced to live in poor conditions, squeezed together with absolute density because of the finite nature of space. Thanks to them death still happens, having survived the test of logic.

Report 2, or The Case Concerning Mr. Home's Fading Identity and the Universal Refrigerator

It was one morning when he stepped into the shower that Mr. Home realized he was slowly disappearing. After being forced into the restroom by his wife, who complained of his foul smell, feeling the sensation of the water drops hitting the surface of his skin, Mr. Home contemplated this queer realization.

"Currently I surely smell," he murmured. "And this water will remove my body odor. Within ten minutes I will emerge from the shower with different attributes, a different aroma, and a different appearance. I will walk to the kitchen, sit on the chair, pull myself toward the table, upon which sit dishes cooked up by my wife that will quickly be integrated into my body and eventually alter the components of my physical structure. I breathe in chemicals as I inhale, lose some as I exhale, and after digesting the food, defecate what used to be contained within me. These things repeat themselves every single day, and slowly my Self is undergoing an irreversible change. What, then, is left of me? Do I persist?" An utter dread made Mr. Home tremble. "I am dying every second."

For several days Mr. Home refused to wash himself, lest his personality slowly melt and disappear into the sewer, intermingled with the scent of Japanese Cherry Blossom. He starved himself, fearing that a mere piece of broccoli might dethrone his ego irreversibly. He managed to hold his bodily defecations, despite some difficulty, safely inside so as not to slowly lose parts of himself. On the third day, when he was seriously considering holding his breath to put a halt to chemical exchange, his wife finally managed to break through the barriers piled in front of the door and emerge into the lightless basement in which Mr. Home confined himself in a desperate attempt to keep away the Reaper.

"Are you okay?" asked his wife, with a concerned look, before adding: "God, you changed a lot."

Then it dawned upon Mr. Home that no matter what, regardless of what he did or how he acted, as long as there was continuous motion, it would be impossible to escape the eventual fading away. This is the crucial moment when the solution struck our wise Mr. Home; he decided to freeze himself, this perpetual and chaotic motion, into a single, timeless moment of graceful permanence. He ran up the stairs, raced into the kitchen, and forced himself into the fridge before slamming the door behind him. After staying in complete darkness for several minutes, however, he became nervous. This, the obvious change in his perception of the world, was a substantial change in his consciousness. Cut off from the rest of reality, he could not see nor hear the things he used to see and hear as Mr. Home. He remembered the cool breeze that often blew on his face as he stood on the front deck of his house on summer nights and the warmth of the vibrant morning star that illuminated the wrinkled face of his dear wife, with whom he had undergone change all his life. All these, yellow trees, chipping birds, apartment buildings, soft drinks, old blue jeans, and everything, all these marvelous things and the vaulting starry heaven itself under which they resided, since they were indispensible components of human life, were all part of Mr. Home's precarious selfhood. Simply preserving his flimsy body of decaying flesh was not enough. He needed a better plan.

"I need a bigger refrigerator," he thought. "The thing has to grow."

For three days and three nights, he sat in the kitchen and worked on the refrigerator, adding things to its delicate mechanical parts and ripping open the circuits. His wife tried to stop him, for if he really did go insane and required intense and costly medical treatments, they certainly couldn't afford another refrigerator. She eventually gave up on that stubborn bastard who had always proven himself counterproductive since the first day they met. On the fourth day, Mr. Home knew that he gave birth to the savior that might save all entities from falling away into an infinite indistinguishable marsh. He gently stroked the surface of that magnificent machine, which was as cold and still as a leaf trapped in ice crystals. He thought of blue sky, birds, the sun and the moon, and other shiny objects scattered across the ancient firmament. He thought of his wife. He thought of the change that added wrinkles on both her face and his, those tiny ripples present on every surface conceivable that slowly faded away. He thought of things that he loved. They did not have to go away. He smiled a smile that would last longer than the oldest surviving civilization, and pressed a conspicuous red button he attached on the left side of the fridge. The machine budged.

Vibration . . .

Vibration . . .

Vibration.

Infinite Silence.

Fifty thousand years later, a group of Wonamurungundi arch priests of the Seventh Dyson Sphere of the eastern galactic realm transmitted the following message at the tip of their great pyramid:

Message sent from: Floating Planetary Observatory

To: God (Yahweh, Allah, Shin, Krishna, Elohim, Odin, Jabberwocky, Wonamundungmundung), our High Creator, perfect among beings, the profound Wellspring of primordial love and Changeless Intellect

Subject: a curious phenomenon concerning celestial glaciation

Approximately two hours and seventy-six minutes ago, one of our drones sensed a substantial drop in the temperature at the southern corner of its universe. We immediately dispatched an investigation team, which observed and confirmed the existence of a refrigerator expanding at the speed of light. The machine's approximate size equals a regular galaxy, and it seems to have an intelligent controller. It's probably another attempt to stop

Change, to whom thy grace gave the power to set everything in motion. We'll just shoot it down.

Report 3, or On One Dying Man's Substantial Self, Which Is a Necktie

Men often forget about their transience. That is why when the realization strikes, it hits them with a peculiar awe. When the Universal Freezing Machine was still in the process of being built, and people were still undergoing infinite changes in their lives, Steve Aquinas, a man full of age, was seated on his bed, and he knew he was about to die. He was very confident about this fact, for his personal physician put it fairly straightforwardly.

"You will cease to exist," she assured him, "within three hours."

This death sentence flooded Steve's heart with thoughts that had never troubled him in his life before.

"I am about to die." He relished the sound. "I will no longer be." He tried to imagine what it would feel like to not exist, but failed. Even a complete black vacuum implied a conscious observer stuck in that darkness. He would simply disappear, and that should be all there was to it. But was that the case? What if a person who died survived the bodily destruction?

"What exactly am I?"

Steve recalled all the different changes he went through during his eventful life. He was born a baby, vulnerable and love-seeking, to a man who hated babies and other love-seeking people and a kind, loving lady who loved both infants and alcoholic beverages but would have chosen the latter if she had to. His days of childhood were not his happiest, and the baby who just arrived on the green planet was forced to adjust to a world that lacked both wealth and care. His fragile personality hardened as he grew in an apathetic world governed by harsh forces, against which he learned man had to fight with both teeth and claws just to remain standing. Like any other being that walked on dry lands, however, Steve too received his share of Fortune's gifts. He saw the girl and immediately knew he owed her a ring. The wedding took place on a graceful summer day. The handsome groom kissed the loving bride, and they lived happily for a long time until their hair turned gray and until the bride eventually hit her seventies and decided to live a more interesting life during her last several years and slept with a cute young man named Ricardo who lived down the street full of loud disco clubs and who was very wise in ways to please mature ladies and followed him to his native Venezuela with half of the groom's net worth. The old man, who was now no longer a husband, was left alone to curse Fortune and the deceptive ways in which She took away everything that in actuality was lent and not given. Even after the divorce, to his surprise, time did not stop, and life happened as it did before. The only difference was that unlike the previous part of his life, the next decade was not a time of experience, growth and gain, but a time of shedding, of letting go. As he sat quietly during his friends' funerals or stood next to the microwave oven staring blankly at the boiling soup, he slowly cast off what he long considered essential parts of himself. He was no longer a young man. He was no longer a husband. He was no longer a friend of any living person. He no longer had erections without pills. Steve was losing characteristics. He was losing everything that he once was.

What was he then?

What was the essential Steve? There must have existed something Steve-like that was able to last amidst the seemingly ceaseless changes of the trivial cover that envelops what is essential to each individual's selfhood: an irreducible and necessary Self. This discovery made him excited. There was a way out of this endless end he was facing. He simply had to find the genuine Steve within him and make sure that it continued to live. It would survive the death of the trivial and accidental form of Steve's body, which would be just another change like countless other changes it already withstood with ease.

For the last two hours and fifty minutes of his life, Steve worked just as diligently in his basement as he did in the days lost in time, and finally managed to complete the most advanced supercomputer the world has ever seen out of a pile of stinking junk he collected in there all his life. The machine, which was an ardent logical positivist as well as a fan of Laplace, would gather every single factual proposition ever generated in human language under the sun, and deduce out of the relevant statements the truth that the questioner was seeking.

Steve turned on the switch and posed the question to that infinite intelligence.

"What am I?"

There was a loud metallic clap as the buzzing computer spit out hot steam and rang the sirens and rocked its heavy body violently, just like they do in the movies to increase suspense. Then, on the tarnished glass screen appeared an image as the black-and-white static slowly faded. It was a little necktie he had received as a little child from his uncle, before all those numerous changes and attainments and loss. He still had it in his old closet he kept since his boyhood. That was him. Steve, for the first time in his entire life, knowingly stared at himself, stripped of unnecessary accessories until the bare image of the Absolute Self emerged. A profound and infinite relief saturated his face as he fell to the ground, a smile of perfect self-realization. In his fading consciousness he contemplated

Steve who was a necktie. As he hung safely in the closet full of old and lasting objects that smelled like mothers in all old memories, Steve was at peace.

Concluding Remarks

O ancient fears and heavenly mysteries of our fathers and mothers passed down through interconnected wombs, forever vibrating through the core of our chests: whence, whence do you spring, and through whose will? Tell me the name of our Maker, Muses, who forges within our fragile selves a piece of Itself that aches and suffers and enjoys and loves and continues singing the songs praising both Creation and Destruction until it finally returns to its origin. In this charming and dangerous place I find myself, and I cannot help but describe, sing, and report through my crude tongue, my dear reader, of the strange events that take place within our universe's life span. We are forever spellbound by stories, and will tell them until the day of our certain death. Until then, may the Most High save our neckties from infinite reapers and expanding refrigerators. Amen.

Voices and Vices

JENNIFER HORSBURGH, Grade 10, Age 15. Newton North High School, Newtonville, MA. Beth Cronin, *Educator*

My mother says, "All you must do is seduce the men. You don't even have to try."

I say, "I'm not old enough yet."

She says, "Yes, you are." Her teeth leave divots in her tight-pressed lips.

I say, "Well, I don't want to." The truth.

She says, "This is what we, the Sirr, do. So shall you." She doesn't say, *You are unnatural* aloud.

I say I don't like their pitiful moans. I say I am disgusted by the sight of their brains spattered on the rocks, the minds they lost to our song split open and strewn when they jumped from the cliffs, mad with the haunting promise of our voices.

She says, "You don't have to look at them, really."

I say, How can I help but see? But our eyes are inconsequential. Our voices are all that matters.

There are tales innumerable about us. We are the wrathful souls of wronged women, condemned to the depths to sing men's deaths. We are the product of deprived men's imaginations, the susurrus voices warbling from the ocean. They loathe us. They crave us. They dispel us from reality, mock us as myth.

We are beings. We are Sirr. That is all. And we are as all other beings are—we simply are. We are born with song thrumming through our blood. Our voices convoke men's vices. But the intensity of our song will kill us if we lock it inside. So we sing. That is all.

The day of my ascending, they bathe and decorate me in silence, two women with gentle hands, with thick hair tinged green. They wrap me in white cloth and lead me to the grotto. For my entrance, all is silent. They withhold their voices in respect, saving them for later, when they will sing for me.

I am shaking. This is not the tickle of anticipatory apprehension that I should feel. This is terror. And it is revulsion. I know what they will say to me, but I don't know what it will do to me. What I will become.

They hum low in their throats, an ululation rising and falling in time with my soaring and stuttering heartbeat.

"Isirra," they whisper, and my name echoes off the walls of the grotto, wreathing its arms around me. "Isirra, Isirra . . ."

"Today you shed your child's name," our eldest woman says. Sirra. Her eyelids are shut, but I believe I can feel her watching me from beneath them. "Today you join our ranks."

The chanting rises to a fever pitch—*"Isirra Isirra Isirra"*—and then falls silent.

"Do you accept your ascension?" Sirra holds out her palms to me, open and smooth, seaweed strung among her fingers.

I swallow. This is the moment where I say no.

"No."

The steady beat of my name falters. Their reverent rhythms are punctuated by gasps.

"Yes," a voice hisses behind me, and my heart crashes. Sirrel. My mother. She shall never permit me to live in the ignominy

I have chosen. That I should have known. She will always be behind me to push me over the edge. "You will ascend if I myself must do it for you."

"You will," I allow. I brace myself.

Her fingernails dig into my back. She shoves me forward, brackets my body with hers, wrenches my arms from my sides and slaps my hands into Sirra's. She holds my wrists with one hand and presses on my throat with the other. I choke out the word they want to hear. "Y-y-yes."

"Then it is done. Isirra, become Sirrai. You are ascended."

The sky is beautiful, an effortless patchwork of cerulean laced with white. The two cliffs between which we make our home border my field of vision, clasping the piece of sky like fisted hands on either side. I float on my back and watch it. I wish for wings to carry me away, instead of a voice that will carry men to death.

A splash beside me, and a friend of mine surfaces. She beams at me and my stomach flutters. She is a year younger and luckier than I—she has one year of her freedom yet, before her song rises to smother her, tears its way from her throat and into the world.

"Hello, Lisirr."

"Have you sung yet, Sirrai?"

I shake my head, and the flutter shrivels. Leave, I will her. I despise her question for its implications, and I despise that it's Lisirr who asks, my friend. She knows how I dread my voice, but she doesn't understand. She never will.

She is the daughter my mother would have loved to be hers.

I have not sung yet. The song is burgeoning within me, forming, preparing to unleash. When it twists its way free, I will not be in control of it. Whenever the song wants to be heard, it will sound. Yet the Sirr revere our voices. Why? Why would we worship that which enslaves us all?

"Look!"

Lisirr points, and I squint. A dark shape on the horizon. The realization is a sick sort of vindicated dread, balled up in my stomach. I cover my eyes in horror, cover my mouth as if that could keep the song in. A ship. A ship approaches; people approach, men. I may sing, and they may die. And if I do not, someone else will, and they will still die. Or they will live long enough to sire more daughters of the Sirr, and then they will die. If not by their own hand, then by their body's betrayal. No one can exist with such poisonous desire. It consumes them, each and every one. They die so we can live.

I want none of it. Not the seduction, not the congress with a man who will father my daughters with his eyes empty, drooling with a desire we force him to feel. Not the weight on my conscience, not the latent poison in my voice.

Lisirr retreats with obvious reluctance; she is not ascended yet, so is forbidden to be above the surface while we sing. The waters around me fill with Sirr. A friction, an anticipation lying heavily over the water. We are silent, waiting, breath bated, song as bait.

The ship is close enough for the first strains of song to reach it. I hear them, high caterwauls to low wails, the purest sweet note to the raging shriek. We sing it all.

Men appear at the railings, bent double over the bars, hands stretching for the sea, mouths agape. The first one falls and my cousin Sirreta leaps and sweeps him under the waves and away. Her song doesn't falter for a single note. Sirr will sing for days, or as long as it takes for the men to have served their purpose. Then we lapse into silence, and as our throats bleed, the delirium of all our sleepless nights claims us. But we are sated. We sleep, recover, repeat.

The men on the ship don't cry out in dismay as their comrade vanishes. Instead, their mewling heightens, tears spilling down their faces. The ship is foundering, turning in circles, listing heavily to the side where the men clutch the railing. Sometimes there are a few who keep their heads when we greet them, who stay at the wheel and move the ship through. They are the men who have no desire for women, whom even we cannot excite, and I love them for it.

This ship is not graced with any who can resist us. It smashes into the shoals that run perilously shallow here. The merciless rocks rend the hull like lightning through clouds, and the men tumble into our water. The Sirr song fades around me as my kin vanish with their prey. In the silence after our song, the men not taken wail, thrashing, as the madness settles into them. The bodies of those who were lucky to die quickly when the ship broke apart float listlessly, blood seeping into the water from gouges up and down their limbs.

I did not sing today. And for that I am grateful, even through my nausea. I take one last look at the corpses, the shattered wood, the setting sun, spilling blood-red rays across this bitter scene. It is for our survival that we sing this destruction into existence, but I have always thought—what kind of survival is it that demands as its price so many guileless lives?

I turn away, draw one more breath of the above-surface air, and dive.

I've barely sunk beneath the surface when it seizes me.

A coil of pain lashes loose inside me and rises up my throat. I choke, scrabble at the water around me, suddenly cold and forbidding. I scream, but it is lost as my song thrusts itself free.

I break the surface again, and I am singing. A screech, a wail, a high and pure melody. I battle as hard as I can, and my tone is flattened, my song compressed, but it will not be stifled.

Tears of exertion stain my face, and I look for the poor man who has evoked this damned song.

In the glare of the sun, I can hardly make out the figure cowering on a sodden slat, once part of the ship's hull. My song hooks its claws into me and pulls, and I swim toward the figure.

He is young. Not yet a man. The sick feeling surges in my throat, but I cannot vomit while singing. The song wins. It always wins.

I am gripping the edge of the slat, tipping it toward me, before I realize.

This victim is no man. No boy, either. It is a girl.

Whose song has ever snared a *girl*?

This, of all things, stops my voice. I choke on the silent syllables, gasp for air as my voice retreats. The fatigue hits with such force that I sag against the board, nearly capsizing it. I cough blood into the water. Tears stream from my eyes. The crash after our first singing is terrible, and no one is supposed to experience it alone.

I'm not alone. I'm with the girl who summoned my song. She's gazing at me, rapt. The delirium is spreading through me, and in my distorted sight she is shimmering and beautiful.

I never knew that our song stirred our own desire, outside of that twisted need . . . I never knew that our songs entrapped us as well.

My arms fall slack against the board the girl is perched on, and my head tips backwards, plunging me momentarily below the surface.

"No, stop!" she says, with alarm. She grasps my arms and pulls me up again, and my skin is fiery where she's holding me. Her voice is hoarse and deep, with an unfamiliar lilt, and her eyes are a murky green when she stares at me. Her skin is a deep amber color I've never seen but on rare sea gems. "Are you dying?"

"No," I rasp, fresh tears spouting as my true voice struggles with my shredded vocal cords. "But you will be, soon."

"Are you . . ."

"Sirr. Yes." Her eyes are curious, not accusing. She's older than I thought. A young woman, not a girl. She surveys the wreckage without sorrow.

"I'm sorry," I manage. The song stirs within me. It was stunned silent, but it will not abate until this girl's life has fed mine. "I'm sorry, I'm sorry . . ."

"Why?" She waves a hand toward the drifting bodies and planks. "They were taking me to be sold as a slave on the far continent. I'm saved now."

"No," I whisper. "We've delivered you from one horror to another. Don't you know what Sirr do? We kill."

She cocks her head. "You haven't killed me. And you're not singing anymore."

"I may start again. I can't control it." I swallow an upsurging of blood.

"Sing for me then, please," she says.

"My song is what will kill you. We kill to stay alive, so our songs don't destroy us from the inside." It's rising again, unfurling its tendrils through me, taking root in a place so deep, excision is impossible. I pull myself onto the board beside her, and it sinks a few inches below the waterline.

My mouth opens and a few hoarse, strangled syllables release. The girl reaches for my hands, and I can see the scant notes already swallowing her. I grit my teeth, and when the song tries to unspool, I bite it back. Pain spreads through my stomach, my throat, all the notes I refuse to sing coalescing in a shrieking headache.

I'm whimpering, bent over beside her, and she's stroking my hair. Who is she? Who would give succor to a woman who's promised her death?

"Sing," she says. "Sing!"

I shake my head violently. *It will kill you. I will kill you. I don't want you to die.* She's resisted my song better than I thought possible up till now, but it will eat her apart if I let it free, it will—

"Sing!"

"No!" I shout, the word breaking free in a howl. Barrier shattered, my song bursts free in a torrent like blood gushing, and I'm possessed of strength enough to sit straight again, the pain receding as my voice commands the night. And the girl.

I sing because I can't not sing, and I sing until my head has cleared enough to see that her eyes are not vacant with cruelly induced, deadly desire, but are shining with lucid awe. She takes my shoulders and moves close to me, her eyes narrowing on mine. My song slips out in a wispy, soft voice, and my hands are trembling, every part of my body commanded by pain moments ago now alive and waiting, breathless. Her lips touch mine, and she swallows my song, cutting it off as I melt toward her. Her hair and clothes are soaked with icy water but her skin is warm and her mouth is hot as the sun. No song tears at me, no discord in my stomach but hunger, true.

We drift. Hours glide by, until the sky is spattered with a trillion sparks of light. The plank knocks ashore at the base of a shallow cave in the cliff face.

We sit at the entrance. Her eyes are alert and full of joy, her arms warm around me, her heartbeat steady. My song is quiet. If I wanted to sing, it would offer itself willingly, but I call it forth, and not the other way round.

I don't know what I will do after tonight. I don't know where we can go. I don't know if I must leave my home, if my refusal to yield to the song will have me exiled. I don't know if I could persuade my kin that there is another way, one less brutal, one with no price to pay for living. One that is beautiful.

I do know what my mother would say. To feel love for our prey is not the goal. That would be unnatural. No, it would be too natural—the only love we are meant to know is that false desire which we force on the men.

But my song is mine, mine to command. I am mine. And I am hers.

My song will never lure a man, will never cause a death. I sing for her alone.

From the Ashes

JULIA BELYUNG, Grade 8, Age 13. Brattleboro Area Middle School, Brattleboro, VT. Joyce Sullivan, *Educator*

We built our civilization on exquisite chemicals. Beautiful mists swirled around cities of crackling sparks and steel, built high above the bubbling lava that warmed our frigid, delicate bodies. Vents that spewed potent, colored plumes of steam into the viscous atmosphere. Vehicles that blazed around the fiery planet, weaving a tapestry of fog that protected us, protected our fragile lungs and throats. Fabulous pools of shimmering rain glimmered in the wide, sparkling streets of a fool's paradise.

We should have known it was not to last.

The cold was patient and subtle. It had always been there, it had always been seeping through the cracks in our perfect world. Yet we were too proud to care. How could something that happened so incredibly slowly ever affect us? To think so was a fanatic's dream, a zealot's distorted cry for attention.

By the time we finally realized the peril, it was too late. We were forced to bore into the planet, into the rock that had been so fiery with energy, but was now dark and bitter. We huddled our tiny civilization next to the feeble core of the earth that had loved us so much, pumping it with our precious chemicals to keep it alive. Waiting, watching for a hope that would never come.

We watched bitterly as the world flooded, as land masses rose like behemoths of gloaming, towering against the frigid waves. We watched as slimy things crawled out and extended writhing feelers, chasing the harsh sun. We watched as the feelers evolved into limbs, and the outlandish creatures learned to carve the bones of the earth, to hunt for sustenance.

We watched our home mutate into an alien planet that learned to grow without us, without the forgotten people that watched it, powerless to help.

Yet there was hope. An offshoot of the outlandish creatures evolved above the others, creating machines to help them surpass their physically stronger brethren. Strange, short-limbed, and incredibly resilient, yet weak against the very chemicals that had nurtured us from birth. They built their own vehicles, wonderful things that scurried like bright jewels, throwing up blankets of comforting smog. And factories were built, with tall rude chimneys that protruded from the hard, cold ground, spewing chemicals that floated high above the earth.

The creatures were as ignorant as we had been, of course. They didn't know they were bringing about the end of their civilization, and a new start for ours. When they did realize, it was far too late.

When at last the wretched things were gone, devoured by the ashes and smoke they had created from a fire of greed, we rose gladly from our living graves. We embraced the whirling fumes, and played with them again as we had when we were young. We were born anew to the many wonders of civilization that we had neglected for so long. We promised ourselves that we would never make that fatal mistake again, that we would be ever watchful. Our planet had not forgotten us.

Sexism in STEM Starts Early—So We Must Combat It Early Too

LIZZIE FIERRO, Grade 11, Age 16. McCallum High School, Austin, TX.
Flor Mota, *Educator*

Enter "scientist" on any Internet image search engine. I'll wait.

Now try "engineer." And "mathematician" too.

What do the most popular results have in common? Notice anything strange?

Most of the people in the photos are middle-aged. Some of the images, particularly those of mathematicians, are simply faded black-and-white photos of long-deceased historical figures. The subjects are also, unsurprisingly, usually white.

And women consistently make up less than one quarter of the first 16 results.

A Widening Gulf

Unfortunately, these search results are indicative of the typical gender disparity in real-world science, technology, engineering, and mathematics (STEM) careers. The National Girls Collaborative Project reports, for instance, that women make up about 22 percent of chemical engineers in the American workforce—the highest number in all of the engineering fields. By contrast, only 5.5 percent of mechanical engineers are women. Meanwhile, according to the president of the Anita Borg Institute for Women and Technology, Telle Whitney, only 20 to 23 percent of Silicon Valley tech workers are women.

And even when women do enter these typically high-paying industries, they often suffer from prejudice surrounding hiring and wage practices. For example, the National Academy of Sciences found in 2012 that faculty members hiring for a lab manager position rated male applicants more favorably than female ones, despite the women having the exact same credentials. In addition, the mean starting salary offered to the men was more than $3,500 higher than that offered to the women.

Clearly, women interested in pursuing STEM careers face numerous obstacles on a systemic level. However, they must also confront biases in individual relationships too. Although boys and girls show equal interest in STEM subjects until about the sixth to eighth grade, those numbers begin to tilt with age in favor of boys. This suggests that attitudes from teachers, parents, other authority figures, and even peers can contribute to this imbalance as early as primary school. Fortunately, with education and awareness, adults can help foster girls' participation in STEM subjects by taking steps to increase their confidence and break down gender stereotypes—and, in turn, create a more equal workforce in the future.

Starting Early

I work at a children's science museum, where every employee orientation includes the same search-engine activity presented at the beginning of this piece. As staff members, we discuss what it means to be a scientist, an engineer, or a mathematician, and how the pervasive, sexist stereotypes of each can affect children in American society.

The stereotypes of what STEM professionals "should" look like are so ingrained into our culture that most parents don't even notice the differences in how they treat their sons and daughters. When the entire world looks a lot like those search-engine results to parents, they can often either consciously or subconsciously reproduce the same social norms in their children. So, in turn, girls who may be just as passionate about dissecting a squid or engineering a paper rocket as boys may eventually begin to confine themselves to explorations of history or literature instead. Of course, not all parents are overtly sexist toward their daughters' interests in STEM subjects. But even those who fail to support young girls' expressed curiosity about science or math contribute to a social dynamic that teaches young girls to pursue other topics.

While subjects like history or art are certainly noble pursuits, as a gallery educator at the museum whose job consists of facilitating activities and interpreting exhibits, I only had to see parents nudge their daughters toward a craft project over a science experiment two or three times to realize that women's unequal participation in STEM subjects is a logical consequence of an entire childhood of conditioning. As a result, I spend a lot of time thinking about how to minimize these micro-aggressions and close the gap between men and women in STEM subjects.

The museum makes heroic efforts toward such a goal: We offer girls-only engineering camps, sponsor events designed to introduce girls to STEM career prospects, and train all employees to recognize the sexism that pervades the scientific field and the early age at which it begins. Officials also teach staff members ways to engage girls during museum-hosted activities. Simply valuing their ideas and allowing them the freedom to work on projects about STEM topics at their own pace can do wonders for girls' enthusiasm; providing a safe environment in which adults prioritize their daughter's explorations may greatly increase girls' desire to pursue STEM subjects further.

However, when our students, who are generally 3 to 8 years old, leave the museum, they'll continue to face ingrained misogyny from a number of fronts. Our anti-sexist efforts, after all, don't continue in every household, and definitely not in every school. According to statistics compiled by the National Girls Collaborative Project, though female high school students take advanced math classes at similar rates to male students, those numbers plummet once young women reach university—suggesting that they face oppressive ideas as young girls and teenagers that emerge when they contemplate their future careers.

I see this trend taking place in my own life too. I'm still in high school, and each year that I take a more advanced math class, I see the number of girls enrolled dwindling. Meanwhile, my ability to relate to my male STEM teachers decreases, as does their support of and encouragement toward me. For example, one instructor spent 20 minutes explaining a problem to a boy while telling me to look in the textbook about the same one; another teacher made assumptions about my future career path, presuming that I would not be interested in a STEM profession even though I'd never indicated a preference toward any particular field. These actions are subtle, but they still undermine the validity of my academic pursuits.

And I'm lucky, because I am passionate—about children, about equal opportunity, and about my own interest in math and science that I noticed shrinking as the people in my life began to guide me toward humanities. Not everyone has the same passion that I have. For that matter, many also do not have access to the information and strategies provided to me and my co-workers in our museum training. That being the case, a great number of people do not have the ability to combat micro-aggressions such as those pervading our homes and classrooms.

A Shift in the System

We need awareness at a broader level. Those of us equipped with information about sexism in STEM need to teach the general public why girls should be encouraged to participate in STEM activities. We need these lessons to be consistently reinforced by adults in the children's lives: parents, teachers, mentors, authority figures, and, of course, museum educators like me.

We must also put pressure on companies in the STEM industry to use their influence to battle sexism. Recently, Google invested $50 million in a coding education initiative for girls, Made With Code. This announcement came shortly after the company revealed that 83 percent of its tech employees are men.

Is 17 percent enough for a company with such reach? No. By making this disclosure and investing their money in this project, though, Google has acknowledged an issue that many companies refuse to touch. Made With Code, aimed at high school girls, will not change the company's employee ratio or the number of female professionals in STEM at Google. But the company is directing its initiative where the seed of interest takes root: youth. With hope, the girls of today will grow into the computer scientists—employed by Google and elsewhere— of tomorrow.

Working to abolish the attitudes and systems that make it difficult for girls to participate in STEM subjects early on will allow girls to gain more confidence and, eventually, higher leadership positions. Including more women may help to expose and resolve systems that are inherently sexist, such as the wage gap, or the practice of hiring men more often than women; it may also discourage sexist micro-aggressions in the workplace that discourage female applicants.

Having more women in STEM fields is important for the entire population, not just those in the industries. After all, men aren't the only ones affected by policies enacted and popularized by science and technology. Increasing the participation of women in STEM careers, for example, would increase the pool of women experts available to rebut unscientific arguments often given by politicians to regulate abortion and contraception. Additionally, the current prejudiced idea that male subjects are the "average" in science would change, which may help to make scientific research and discoveries safer for women. Recently, the National Institutes of Health adopted a policy that explicitly works toward the inclusion of females in scientific studies. We need more of this.

Perhaps if schools, individuals, and organizations across the country commit to combating misogyny, our scientists, our engineers, and our mathematicians will eventually defy the stereotype that Google Images itself reinforces—proving that our STEM professionals do not have to be one age, one race, and certainly not one gender.

The Favor

JACK FOSSETT, Grade 11, Age 17. School for Creative and Performing Arts, Cincinnati, OH. Wendy Braun and Mary Lenning, *Educators*

EXT. TAIPEI NIGHT MARKET—NIGHT

[A large number of vendors are piled into a small street and the space between their kiosks is filled with people, mostly TOURISTS, shuffling and bustling, searching for a good deal amongst an endless sea of cheap trinkets. GIRL, nine or ten years old and American, looks lost in the middle of the crowd, but maneuvers through the hordes of people like she knows exactly where she's going. Her shoes are poorly tied and her socks do not match.

She makes her way to a makeshift ARCADE at the end of the market, where crude balloon darts and water gun target shooting GAMES are set up. One vendor has a plastic KIDDIE POOL full of small GOLDFISH. GIRL walks up to him as he is shouting to the crowd, pitching his game.]

FISH VENDOR
(to passers-by, ad-libbed)
Fishing, fishing, would you like to go fishing? Win your very own pet fish, they are good luck! etc.

[GIRL approaches the man and taps him on the arm.]

GIRL
Can I play?

[The vendor spins around to see GIRL, stunned that anyone is actually asking to play.]

FISH VENDOR
Of course! Thirty dollars for every dip. You keep what you catch.

[GIRL pulls out her wallet and hands the FISH VENDOR thirty (New Taiwan) dollars and grabs a net. She fishes around for a minute before pulling the net out of the water. There is a single fish in it, and it is clearly dead. GIRL smiles. The vendor frowns.]

FISH VENDOR (CONT'D)
Sorry, little girl. Maybe next time.

GIRL
But I caught one!

FISH VENDOR
You don't want a dead fish, that's nonsense. I'll tell you what—you can try again if you want to. No charge.

GIRL
Can I just have the fish? I caught it. You said I got to keep what I caught.

FISH VENDOR
But why do you want this one?

GIRL
I won it fair and square! Just give it to me, please.

[FISH VENDOR sighs and takes the net from GIRL. He dumps the DEAD FISH into a clear PLASTIC BAG. The DEAD FISH floats belly-up. GIRL eagerly grabs the PLASTIC BAG. She walks back through the market streets. She passes beggars, barbers, musicians, and small boutiques, but the streets are mostly filled with food vendors. One vendor's kiosk looks particularly enticing. GIRL stops at a custard-filled pancake stand.]

GIRL (CONT'D)
(to DEAD FISH)
These used to be my mom's favorite. Do you want any?

[DEAD FISH floats in the bag. GIRL waits for a response, then shrugs and turns to the vendor. She points to a picture of a fish-shaped pancake.]

GIRL (CONT'D)
Six, please.

CUSTARD VENDOR
Fifty dollars.

[GIRL hands the vendor fifty dollars and waits. The vendor collects the CUSTARD FISH in a BOX and hands it to GIRL. She opens the BOX and eats one of the CUSTARD FISH.]

GIRL
(to DEAD FISH)
Are you sure you don't want one? They're delicious.

[GIRL takes the BOX of CUSTARD FISH in one hand and the BAG with the DEAD FISH in the other. She walks to the end of the street market and down a flight of stairs to a train station.]

INT. TAIPEI MAIN STATION—NIGHT

[GIRL rides down the ESCALATOR to the platform and waits for the MRT. The station is mostly empty because it is fairly late at night. The train arrives and GIRL hurries on.]

INT. MRT CAR—NIGHT

[GIRL sits in a train car, which is fairly crowded. She finds an empty seat next to a YOUNG WOMAN who appears to be dressed for an office job, holding a purse. GIRL places the bag holding the DEAD FISH on her lap. The train starts to move, and they sit in silence for a moment. GIRL turns to the DEAD FISH.]

GIRL
I know you're dead.

[The DEAD FISH floats in the bag, silently.]

GIRL (CONT'D)
But I hope I can still get through to you.

[The DEAD FISH floats in the bag, silently.]

GIRL (CONT'D)
I used to have my own pet fish. I named her Melissa, after my mom, because my daddy bought her for me after she moved back home. I loved her so much, maybe to death. I did everything right. I fed her, I cleaned her bowl, I gave her rocks to play with. But one day I came home from school and she was floating on top of the water. Kind of like you are now. My daddy said it was because she got sick.

[YOUNG WOMAN glances over at GIRL and pulls her purse closer. GIRL does not notice.]

GIRL (CONT'D)
You remind me of her.

[They sit in silence for a moment as the train rattles. A woman's voice comes over a loud speaker in the car.]

PRE-RECORDED FEMALE ANNOUNCER (V.O.)
Now approaching Xinpu Station. Next stop: Banqiao Station.

[The train stops. The doors open. The YOUNG WOMAN switches seats. No one in the crowded car claims her seat.]

GIRL
I know this probably looks bad, but they aren't real fish. They actually taste very good. I think you'd like them if you tried one.

[The DEAD FISH floats in the bag, silently.]

GIRL (CONT'D)
Oh, right.

[The doors close. The train begins to move again. GIRL stares forward for a moment, thinking.]

PRE-RECORDED FEMALE ANNOUNCER
Now arriving at Banqiao Station. Next stop: Fuzhong Station.

GIRL
This is us.

INT. BANQIAO STATION—NIGHT

[GIRL picks up the BAG with the DEAD FISH and the half-empty BOX. She exits the train car and throws the BOX away.]

GIRL
I don't know why I always think I can eat all six of those by

myself. They're too sweet.

[Now holding only the DEAD FISH, GIRL takes the ESCA-
LATOR to the ground level. She walks through the station,
which is mostly empty, until she reaches . . .]

EXT. NEW TAIPEI CITY HALL—NIGHT

[GIRL walks up a semi-circular stairway and into an open
CITY SQUARE in front of NEW TAIPEI CITY HALL. The
square has a public garden with FOUNTAINS and BRIDGES—
she walks right through it. She continues to walk through the
city for a few blocks, until she turns to walk down an alley.
She unlocks the door to a gray concrete apartment building
and enters.]

GIRL
(to DEAD FISH)
I have a favor to ask of you. You don't mind, do you? Good, I'd
hate to be a bother.

[She walks into the building. The door shuts behind her.]

INT. STAIRWELL—NIGHT

[GIRL enters her apartment building. There is no elevator, so
she starts to walk up the stairs.]

GIRL
Remember that fish I brought up earlier—Melissa? And
remember how she's dead? Well, since you're dead too, I was
hoping you could talk to her for me.

[There is a plaque on the wall indicating that they have
reached floor two.]

GIRL (CONT'D)
That's not offensive, is it? I don't mean that I think all dead fish know each other or anything—I know there are a lot of you, and it's impossible to know everyone, but I was just hoping—I mean, can you?

[Floor three.]

GIRL (CONT'D)
I can get you to where she is so you can talk to her. I'll even tell you what to say. It won't be hard, I promise.

[Floor four. GIRL stops, fishes around for her KEYS and unlocks her apartment door. She slides off her shoes and steps inside. There are no other shoes by the door.]

GIRL (CONT'D)
Well, this is it.

INT. APARTMENT—NIGHT

[The apartment is very sleek and modern. It looks expensive, unlike the exterior of the building. GIRL sets the DEAD FISH on a clear glass coffee table. She looks at the clock on the wall. There is a picture next to it, featuring GIRL, her father, and her mother. Her eyes linger on the photograph, but only for a moment.]

GIRL
It's very late, I bet my dad is worried.

[She sticks her head into her dad's bedroom.]

GIRL (CONT'D)
I'm home, Daddy! I'm safe.

[There is no one there. She looks in the kitchen next.]

GIRL (CONT'D)
Daddy? Hello? Oh.

[She sighs, then returns to the coffee table and sits on a black leather sofa.]

GIRL (CONT'D)
He's probably still working. That means it's just you and me, Fish. Do you want anything for dinner?

[The DEAD FISH floats in the bag, silently.]

GIRL (CONT'D)
Right, of course not. I guess there's no use in waiting, then.

[She picks up the DEAD FISH and takes him to the bathroom.]

INT. BATHROOM—NIGHT

[GIRL lifts the toilet seat and sits on the floor, facing the bowl. She carefully unties the plastic bag and lets the contents spill into the toilet. DEAD FISH splashes into toilet water, settles.]

GIRL
When Melissa died, my daddy flushed her down this toilet. He said it goes to fish heaven. I'm going to flush you down the same toilet so you can be in the same part of fish heaven. That way it'll be easier for you to find her.

When you do find her, I want you to tell her I miss her. Tell her Daddy misses her too. Sometimes he still cries about it. Say, "You were loved, Melissa. Loved to death." She would probably laugh at that. Tell her I wish I had been there to say goodbye. Tell her I'm sorry if the toilet water was too cold or too warm when she was flushed—she deserved nothing but the best.

But most importantly, please tell her that I didn't replace her. She kept me company when she was alive, and she probably thinks that I got another fish as soon as she died. I bet she thinks that fish is named Melissa II, and I'm watching it swim right now. But even thinking about replacing her feels wrong. I'd much rather be lonely than betray an old friend. We were too close for me to just move on like that.

Did you get all of that? Please don't forget anything. And please enjoy fish heaven.

[GIRL flushes the toilet. Water circles the toilet bowl and the DEAD FISH spins in the current, limp like a rag doll. As the water recedes, the fish is pulled under. The flush is complete. There is no more water in the toilet bowl. No more DEAD FISH. GIRL gets up and walks from the bathroom, into . . .]

INT. GIRL'S BEDROOM—NIGHT

[GIRL opens the door to her bedroom. Like the rest of the apartment, the floor is white tile. Her bed is plain and fitted with pink sheets. The room's decor seems too childish; it does not suit her.

She opens a large wooden armoire and changes into her pajamas quickly and silently. She climbs into bed and pulls the comforter up to her chin. She turns to her bedside table, on which there is an empty fish bowl and a framed picture of GIRL with her mother. She reaches out to touch it.]

GIRL
Goodnight.

FADE TO BLACK.

The War on Modern Boy Bands: In Defense of Teenage Girls

CAROLINE TSAI, Grade 11, Age 16. Canterbury School, Fort Wayne, IN. John McRae, *Educator*

I know two words that will make almost anybody roll their eyes.

Boy band.

Anyone living in the Western hemisphere within the past 50 years can instantly conjure up the archetype of the boy band. Three to six angel-voiced, barely pubescent boys posed with arms crossed in front of their chests or on each other's shoulders, holding microphones or guitars. They have pouty lips and puppy-dog eyes. The 2014 version has the boys wearing skinny jeans and old school Chuck Taylor sneakers, poised between experience and innocence, with androgynous tattoos and luxuriant hair. They're modeling on the covers of teen magazines and tabloids. They're being interviewed on morning talk shows. They're the top draw at charity events. And on the off chance that the tabloids run out of photos, there they are, exiting limos, shading their eyes from paparazzi flashes.

Boy bands are not a new phenomenon. In the 1960s, there was John, Paul, George, and Ringo. Flash-forward to the 1990s—the boy band is revived by *NSYNC, the Backstreet Boys, the Hansons, New Kids on the Block, and Take That, to name a few. And today, teenage girls have the likes of One Direction and 5 Seconds of Summer.

Critics of the boy band may focus on the vacuous music or their fashion or looks, but more and more, criticism has turned toward their fans, who, more likely than not, are teenage girls. This criticism often has a condescending, patronizing tone. The criticism assumes the worst about girls. Moreover, it is omnipresent; teen girls not only hear it in school or at home, but are judged by every form of media: radio, newspaper, magazine, morning talk shows, and social media outlets. Everyone over the age of twenty has an opinion about boy bands and their fans, and feels entitled to lecture teen girls about it.

From an outside perspective, I understand why people dislike the obsessive nature of the fan base. Think about it: teenage girls who are willing to stay up all night for a new album, or camp out for hours in front of a hotel in a foreign city, all for a group of boys. Strangers! Boys they will never know and never talk to. Celebrities hyped by a tireless publicity machine. Huge stadiums and arenas—literally, a whole football field's worth of teenage girls—filled with hysterical fans willing to pay hundreds of their parents' dollars to see their favorite band.

Screaming. A whole lot of screaming.

It sounds crazy, but fangirls are a long-standing tradition in human history. In ancient Greek mythology, Dionysus was the god of wine and chaos. The Greeks attributed the sensual, instinctive, joyful, and chaotic characteristics of human nature to him. He was the party god. Dionysus stars as the protagonist in the famous play by Euripides, *The Bacchae*. He takes revenge on the city Thebes because the king did not believe that Dionysus was the son of Zeus. Dionysus drives the women of the city mad, including his three aunts. The women are observed singing and dancing in the woods around the city, suckling wild wolves and gazelles, making milk and honey spring out of the ground, devastating villages and ripping to shreds any animals in their way. Ultimately, the king and his kingdom are destroyed when the king's mother, in a trance, kills her son with her bare hands. The play is a warning not to ignore the irrational side of human nature—and Euripides famously used a large group of women, possessed by a supernatural being, to demonstrate it.

So the criticism against fanatical females goes back a long way. But in the case of boy band fans, we have to ask ourselves: Why are we so quick to silence them? Their behavior might be extraordinary or excessive, but it's otherwise harmless. Fans who go to stadiums in droves, buy expensive merchandise, cheer and cry for the stars—don't they act exactly like sports fans? But in society, we tolerate sports fans with good humor and crucify girls.

As a teenage girl, I can tell you honestly that in the eyes of society, teenage girls can do no right. Magazines, television, and advertisements tell teenage girls what they're supposed to like and what they're not supposed to like. These advertisements play on the natural insecurities of a girl as she changes through puberty, challenging her self-image, criticizing her for maturing too fast and not maturing fast enough, for being too flirty, for being haughty. Words that describe a girl's attitudes: snobbish, stuck-up, loose, easy, fake—are weighted with judgment, and are meant to kill her self-esteem. If she buys into what's being advertised, she's an idiot who's just hopping on the bandwagon and a crazy fangirl. If she's interested in something different—say, video games or science fiction—she's dubbed a "fake geek girl" and a "nerd." There is no middle ground—a girl is either gullible or dishonest. After a while, she no longer tries to defend herself. Internalized misogyny is so prevalent that she begins to believe it.

Teenage girls are the easiest to criticize and the most vulnerable, which is why we as a society should stop abusing them at every turn. Take it from me: Teenage girls are at a stage in their lives when they are constantly thinking about what other people think of them. *Does he think I'm stupid? Fat? Stuck-up? Weird? What do they think about me? How can I change to seem better? How can I blend in? How can I stand out? I mean, in a good way?*

Boy bands provide an outlet for teenage girls who are seeking reassurance and acceptance. "I know you've never loved / The crinkles by your eyes / When you smile / You've never loved / Your stomach or your thighs / The dimples in your back at the bottom of your spine / but I'll love them endlessly," sings Liam Payne in "Little Things." The underlying message of most of their songs is that you don't have to change to be accepted—you will be loved and accepted, just the way you are.

In July 2013, the members of One Direction were the cover stars of *GQ* magazine. The photography was professional and beautiful. However, Jonathan Heaf's accompanying article came under fire for implying that the band members were womanizers, and the fan base was a cult of hormonal, sex-crazed teenagers. Heaf wrote, "By now, we all know the immense transformative power of a boy band to turn a butter-wouldn't-melt teenage girl into a rabid, knicker-wetting banshee who will tear off her own ears in hysterical fervor when presented with the objects of her fascinations."

It got worse. Heaf described the concert as "a dark pink oil slick that howls and moans and undulates with every impish crotch-thrust from their idols' plinths. Thousands of female fans caught on the cusp of their own sexual awakening."

The fans were furious, and for good reason. Heaf's usage of sexualized language to describe teenage girls, especially coming from a 34-year-old man, wasn't just wrong—it was creepy. Tumblr user cherrybina posted, "I want girls to be furious at the rampant misogyny and absolute contempt for teenage girls in this article . . . the phrase 'teenage girl' was an insult long before [One Directon] came along."

Heaf's generalization that all fans of the band are sexually attracted to the boys is presumptive, harmful, and blatantly inaccurate. As impossible as it may sound to Heaf, people, both men and women, of all sexual orientations love boy bands. It's unfair to assume that everyone who knows the words to "What Makes You Beautiful" wants to sleep with Harry Styles. The message of the song is an empowering one, and it obviously spoke to the fans.

So, what about the girls who actually *are*, as Heaf writes, "caught on the cusp of their own sexual awakening?"

Well, what's so wrong with that? Girls' harmless crushes on boy bands provide a safe means of exploring their sexuality and romantic preferences. They find out what they like, what they want in a future relationship, and how it feels to date a boy, all from a safe distance. The songs teach that there is more than one way—the sexual way—for a boy to see a girl. Beauty may be more than merely physical. Isn't that a worthwhile way for girls to see themselves? We have to consider the alternative here: Teenage girls discover their sexual awakenings from real-life teenage boys, who will demand real-life sexual favors and might not practice safe sex. Makes the boys on the radio sound like saints, doesn't it?

As Professor Rachel Karniol writes in *Adolescent Females' Idolization of Male Media Stars as a Transition Into Sexuality*, "Media stars are preferable as love objects because they are inaccessible, can serve as practice love objects on which to test new exciting feelings, to discuss and legitimize these feelings in one's peer group, to play-act the role of caring for someone else, and fantasize about being loved back." It might be synthesized love, but it is a safe step toward learning about real love.

Besides, do teenage fans of One Direction really believe that they are in love with band members? Critics like Heaf have implied that fans, like the Bacchae in Euripides' play, are incapable of separating reality from fantasy. On the contrary: through social media sites like Tumblr and Twitter, fans share awkward photos of One Direction members and their girlfriends. The fans know that band members (who, after all, were discovered on a reality TV show) are real people, and do not take the band members too seriously. Amanda Hess, writing in *Slate*, believes that both boy bands and their fans have changed since the 1990s. When she compared music videos from the two periods, she found One Direction videos to be funnier, sillier, less erotic, and in general, happier than their predecessors. She writes, "Today's young women are freed to see sex and love and friendship as more interconnected than they were before." Despite societal pressures, teenage girls have evolved to regard boys as equals. They view the band with some ironic self-awareness, as band members view themselves.

And finally, has anyone noticed that the sexual awakening of teenage girls is the only sexual awakening being criticized? When boys talk about pornography, it's totally normal—in fact, it's an implicit coming-of-age ritual. In romantic comedies, male interest in pornography is frequently bantered about in a good-natured, frat-house, "boys will be boys" kind of way. When girls suggest that Harry Styles is cute, they're suddenly deemed abnormal, sex-crazed hormonal creatures with illegitimate interests. They must be shamed and punished for showing any attraction to a boy. It's a pervasive double standard that perpetuates the societal epidemic of rape culture. Is this really what we want to teach teenage girls?

It's my hope that society reconsiders its opinion on boy bands and their fans—for its own sake, but more importantly, for the sake of teenage girls. It's also my hope that teenage girls ignore the h8rs and continue to be unabashedly enthusiastic about what they love. ~~Even if~~ *Especially* if it involves some fangirling.

TAYLOR AGEE, *DISorder*, Grade 12, Age 17. Burton Center for Arts & Technology, Salem, VA. Patricia Carr, *Educator*. American Visions Award

The Road to Tomorrow: Focusing on Localized Development to Combat Poverty

CHRIS WANG, Grade 10, Age 15. Mission San Jose High School, Fremont, CA. Katherine Geers, *Educator*

"If I focus on the one, I may not have much impact, but if I focus on the many, I may help an entire community prosper." —Mother Teresa

The road to town seemed endless. An excruciating pain radiated from her bare feet. With every step, the bamboo basket loaded with tea leaves felt heavier on her back. After tramping on the pebble road under the scorching sun for ten hours, the girl reached deep into her pocket for a wrinkled bill, debating whether to use it to get on the bus or buy some water. Eventually, she decided to save it. A roadside vendor peddled food to her. She waved back with a smile. She had reason to be happy— if she sold all the tea leaves on her back in town, she could pay for a two-day train ride to see her parents.

On that burning summer day, how she wished her parents did not have to make a living in a faraway city so that she could see them more often than once every six months. How she wished there was a tea factory near her village so that she did not have to carry tea leaves to town basket by basket. How she wished she had a little extra change left so that her journey to town could be less agonizing.

She was not alone. Because of poverty, hundreds of millions of children around the globe suffer from hunger, illness, separation, illiteracy, and other miseries. Because of poverty, they grow up without access to opportunities, end up living the same hopeless lives as their parents, and eventually pass the same hopeless lives on to their own children.

For that little girl, fortunately, her fate was miraculously changed thanks to sweeping economic reforms in her country. Thirty years later, she returned with her child to that once-rugged country road in rural China. The craggy trail was long gone, replaced by a four-lane paved road surrounded by fields of tea trees. The once destitute village had been transformed into a bustling tea-producing hub lined with modern buildings. Seeing the barely contained excitement bursting from her eyes at that moment, I was profoundly shaken. She is my mother.

In the past three decades, the world has come a long way in combating poverty. From 1980 to 2010, the percentage of people living in extreme poverty in developing countries fell from more than 50% to 21%—a reduction of more than 1 billion people. Are the citizens of the world succeeding in reducing poverty? The numbers seem to suggest yes. No one can deny the massive improvements that have taken place in the lives of many people around the world during the past couple of decades. However, if we look carefully at the data, we see that the vast percentage drop in poverty worldwide was brought largely by the sharp poverty reduction achieved in East Asia, particularly, China. In many parts of the developing world, poverty has continued and worsened, as many countries struggle constantly to maintain economic and social stability. Even in countries that have seen success in poverty reduction, new issues, such as escalating gaps between the rich and the poor, have emerged, causing new plights for combating poverty.

Today, how can the world effectively and efficiently reduce poverty?

Poverty can be caused by one or a combination of complicated factors, such as unemployment, low wages, education deficiencies, regional economic disasters, diseases, and broken government systems. Since poverty has different causes as it affects each individual, it is impossible to develop a universal way to reduce poverty for every individual. On the other hand, individuals in a specific group or area usually suffer from poverty as a result of the same social economic problems pertaining to that particular group or area. Thus, when we study and develop models to reduce poverty, we should look at reducing poverty for a specific group or area. When a group or area is empowered and transformed, individuals belonging to that group or area will survive and thrive.

It helps to learn from those who have achieved marked success in poverty reduction. China, for example, implemented policies encouraging localized economic development as a way of combating poverty in the 1990s. Coastal areas of China utilized their geographic and resource advantages to develop a manufacturing economy, while the inland areas focused on an agricultural economy based on local products. Consequently, the country's poverty rate was sharply reduced. China's experience shows that to enrich a group or area, the key is to fuel the group or area with economic vitality and strength based on its own resources.

Indeed, localization is the easiest and fastest way to jumpstart an economy. There is no easier strategy to grow a tea village's economy than to establish tea processing and distribution centers at the village. There is no faster way to improve a fishing island's livelihood than to build seafood processing facilities on the island. There is no better solution to enhance the well-being of a cotton farming area than to develop textile industry in the area. In other words, by utilizing local resources, businesses can take shape and create employment within the shortest period of time. By having continuous access to local resources, businesses can best facilitate reproduction processes, allowing them to sustain, expand, and prosper.

Therefore, to best combat poverty, we should focus on fostering localized development activities based on the economic viability and resources of a particular group or area. With business development and employment creation, local residents will stay and new people will arrive. Soon, a strong local community will form: Schools will be created, hospitals will be built, housing will be constructed, and the infrastructure will be developed. As a result, poverty will be gone.

As this strategy emphasizes localized economic development, the key to its implementation comes down to two vital details: business creation in a particular location and funding for the particular location. Both are feasible, especially with government support.

First, localized economic development has an advantage in attracting businesses. In a market economy, businesses have a natural tendency to operate in an area that has resource or location advantage for developing or distributing a particular product, as it gives the business an edge over competitors. In addition, to encourage businesses to operate in a particular location, the government can offer policy and market support. For established businesses, the government can encourage them to open facilities by providing tax incentives, market benefits, and credit enhancement. For new businesses, the government can work with private sectors to provide technical and business assistance in addition to tax, market, and credit incentives. With incentives from both local resources and government policies, business creation for localized economic development is practical, viable, and predictable.

Further, localized economic development is in a good position to obtain funding. As this strategy brings economic development as well as poverty reduction, it fits under the auspices of both economic development programs and poverty reduction programs. Thus, there are more funding opportunities for this strategy than other poverty reduction protocols that aim solely to lessen poverty. Governments, international organizations, and private foundations all have funding programs specifically for both economic development and poverty reduction. Moreover, the government can encourage large corporations to help fund localized development by offering tax incentives, public relations benefits, and government project advantages. When the government does not act alone, but as a leader among private entities and nongovernment organizations, the goal of funding localized development is easily achievable.

Therefore, with government support, focusing on localized economic development is not only efficient and effective in combating poverty, but also feasible to implement.

The objective of this strategy is to create direct and fast changes in specific localities; thus, its outcomes are easily measurable. The impacts of localized development can be assessed economically and socially. Economically, it creates businesses and enhances wealth for the area; it generates employment and provides income for the families in the area; it trains the labor force and enables individuals in the area to survive and thrive. Socially, it improves communal conditions, such as infrastructures, healthcare, and education, and thus promotes societal advancement; it develops a strong community and thus fosters community cohesion; it reduces migration to certain urban areas and thus enhances social stability. All of these will undoubtedly bring real and solid changes to the lives of people in the area. In case the expected outcomes are not achieved, or there are any problems in achieving the expected outcomes, the fact that this strategy focuses on and takes place within a specific locality makes it straightforward for stakeholders to assess and resolve the issues.

Likewise, this strategy can be applied to most impoverished areas around the world simply because it is about economic and social improvements for a specific locality. Regardless of the socio-economic environment, regardless of the geographic location, and regardless of the level of poverty, there is no better protocol to combat poverty than starting from the grassroots—boosting economic and community independence based on local resources and environment. In urban inner cities, localized development involves creating city-oriented employment projects at the heart of the slums so that the homeless and the hopeless can have access to job opportunities and job training. In high-unemployment suburbs, localized development means utilizing the suburbs' location to develop employment centers so that the poor and the unemployed can gain financial independence. In the rural countryside of developing countries, localized development entails deploying the countryside's resources to grow agricultural or other businesses so that the indigent and the destitute can achieve self-sufficiency. In regions stricken by a natural or economic disaster, localized development stands for actions by the international community to provide the humanitarian and financial support most needed by the region at a particular time so that the devastated and the distressed can obtain timely help.

Additionally, the emergence of a global economy provides a great opportunity for applying this strategy on a global scale. A global market frees businesses from concerns about the limitations of local markets, motivating them to make commitments based on local resources regardless of the local consumption capacity. A global market opens doors for products and services of localized economies to all corners of the world, enhancing the sustainability of localized economies. Moreover, in a global economy, the relatively low labor cost in impoverished areas becomes an incentive for cost-sensitive businesses to divert their labor-intensive operations to these areas, and as a result, the scope of business that can be undertaken in an impoverished area is broadened.

In the United States, efforts on poverty reduction have traditionally concentrated on providing monetary or material aids to individuals or families who are identified as below a certain income level. In fiscal year 2014, the U.S. federal, state, and local governments spent $493.6 billion on welfare and related assistance programs. There is no doubt that such assistance provides temporary relief to individuals who are in need. But does welfare really solve the problems that make people "poor" and thus reduce poverty? According to data released by the U.S. Census Bureau, from 1981 to 2011, the U.S. poverty rate remained the same, at about 15% of the country's population (based on U.S. poverty standard). By contrast, during the same thirty-year period in China, the poverty rate was reduced from 84% to 10% of the country's population (based on international poverty standard). As noted above, China's success in poverty rate reduction came from its policy of fostering localized development that empowered local communities to achieve self-sufficiency. The secret of lifting people out of poverty is to eradicate the root of their poverty—to provide a localized environment for them to gain economic independence. To better combat poverty in the U.S., all levels of the government, along with the many U.S. organizations that have been making tremendous efforts in reducing poverty, should consider the strategy of focusing on localized development as a supplement to the existing social assistance programs. If the government takes initiative to stimulate and nurture localized economies in distressed parts of the country, we are bound to see great improvements in poverty reduction in the U.S. in the near future—we are bound to see a path forward.

The road to town widened ahead, extending to the horizon, as I stood silently by my mother in the once poverty-stricken countryside. The girl who once struggled on the road, carrying tea leaves basket by basket, had a future, and so should hundreds of millions of boys and girls around the globe who are struggling in poverty every day. It is time to take action and end the cycle of poverty. If we focus on the grassroots of every impoverished community by fostering localized economic and social development, then for every destitute village, for every indigent child, there is a road to a bright tomorrow.

Visit **www.artandwriting.org/galleries** for the bibliography.

All Hail King Bezos

ALISON BOEHMER, Grade 12, Age 17. Nixa High School, Nixa, MO.
Lori Joynes, *Educator*

It is 1994. A rosy-cheeked, seven-year-old bookworm slams the door of her family's Ford Taurus and darts across the Barnes & Noble parking lot, ignoring her mother's pleas to hold her hand. Her eyes double in size as her disgruntled Keds bring her to a halt under the neon sign plastered to the warehouse-size retail building. She musters all of her might to swing open the massive doors. Immediately, the crisp smell of black coffee and ink overwhelm her nostrils, and she cannot help but to release a grin. Her mother, out of breath and unhappy with her daughter's choice to cross the lot unattended, catches up and begins to lecture her. The young girl's ears hear only muffled sounds as her sneakers, as if by their own will, quickly walk her to the corner of the store labeled "Children's."

It is 2014. A freckled seven-year-old trudges up his driveway, scuffing his Nike Free Runs against the pavement. He jerks the door handle and whips his backpack onto the floor in one, routine motion. Instantly, the smell of his mother's homemade spaghetti sauce invites him into the kitchen. He practically sprints for the countertop that houses his e-reader and instinctively logs into his account with a few swift touches to the screen. His mind is already checked out of his suburban living room and into the enticing fictional world by the time he reaches the couch; he only faintly hears his mother's spitting of questions as he adjusts the screen's brightness and settles into "Chapter Four."

There is no doubt that the environment of reading has changed: It is more common for pages to be downloaded than turned; books are bought online versus in line; and best sellers find their fame based on how many customers click the BUY button. This monstrous shift in the industry coincides with the shift in society brought on by the Internet and the resulting technological uprising. Innovative and bold entrepreneurs, such as Steve Jobs and Bill Gates, are credited with contributing to this upheaval of traditions and surge of technology; Jeff Bezos and Amazon.com have undoubtedly had their part in this revolution. Through Amazon's discounted prices, innovative features, and e-book revolution, the company has taken both the book-selling and publishing industries by storm.

Setting the Scene: Book Retailers and Publishers Pre-Amazon

The Pre-Amazonian era (which will most definitely be found in history books come 2050) was one of much consumer contentment and industry executive unrest, which is typical in a trade that is controlled entirely by marketers chasing after consumers' recreational dollars. Publishers and retailers alike were, much like today, constantly searching for strategies to catch the attention of customers. Little did they know that a massive shift that would forever shake the book industry was about to be introduced by a small, bald man with an Amazon-sized dream.

Selling the Future

Until the entrance of Amazon onto the book-selling scene,

consumers were accustomed to waiting in line at their local Barnes & Noble superstore to purchase the new Harry Potter novel while grasping their freshly made caffeinated beverage that had been conveniently brewed in-house. Large-scale bookstores were the name of the game, and Barnes & Noble and Borders were essentially the only two players. Independent booksellers were crying "monopoly" to the authorities through legal suits, claiming that the two powerhouses had a stronghold on the industry and were exhorting unreasonable discounts from wholesalers. The suits warranted little but a slap on the wrist to the two companies, as the authorities realized that consumers were pleased with the ease and convenience provided by these monstrous bookstores that housed more than 175,000 titles. American book connoisseurs had become comfortable with the luxuries that these monstrosities enabled; they were satisfied with the enticing rows upon rows of books and hot beverages readily available. Consumers were content; Barnes & Noble and Borders were thrilled. The sounds of satisfied readers were loud enough to drown out the cries of independent bookstores, and there was peace within the book-selling kingdom.

Enter: Amazon.

Publishing Houses Crouch in Their Corners

Picture this: Six monstrous, luxurious houses reside peacefully on a quiet countryside, happily dictating to the quainter residences living in the meek village below them. The occasional uprising from the subordinate houses is easily squelched with a harsh glare; no one dares to protest their superiority, for they have controlled the entire kingdom for generations. Just when the six houses think they have a permanent chokehold on the entire kingdom, an innovative entrepreneur buys a plot of land neighboring their domain. This man sees little value in merely competing with these houses; instead, he decides to revolutionize the entire system. He, seeing beyond the limits of traditional mansion-style housing, builds a hovering, mobile metropolitan utopia, complete with a water park made of liquid chocolate. The six houses, though still powerful, quiver in fear of this new neighbor and his unconventional ideas. They, for the first time, feel threatened and small in comparison to the "new kid on the block," as they certainly do not have a water park made of liquid chocolate.

The above illustration portrays the state of the book publishing industry in the Pre-Amazonian era. The original "six houses" represent the world's dominating publishing houses: Hachette Book Group, HarperCollins, Macmillan, Penguin Group, Random House, and Simon & Schuster. Represented through the "subordinate houses" are independent publishers, who have been threatened to be made obsolete since the rising of the "Big Six." Obviously, the "new neighbor" is Jeff Bezos and Amazon; the "water park" could be a number of revolutionary features offered through Amazon, such as digital publications, self-publishing, and attractive royalties. As in the story, the Big Six greatly fear Bezos, for he continually threatens their way of business and cares little about the status quo.

A clear and startling manifestation of Amazon's dominance can be seen through the recent consolidation of Penguin and Random House. The fact that these powerhouses felt that the only way to survive in a world with Amazon was to swallow their prides and join forces exemplifies the iron fist with which Bezos rules. Both the Big Six and Amazon's respective checking accounts further prove the behemoth's control over the industry: In 2011, Amazon's revenue of $48 billion was more than the conglomerate total of the world's largest houses. As a result of Amazon's dominance and variety of "water parks," the Big Six are now viewed as the lesser of two evils by independent book publishers.

Amazonian Discounts

The intense draw to Amazon's products and a key to the company's success results from its unparalleled prices, which enable the company to elbow competition away from bargain-hungry consumers. In traditional publishing, bookstores keep typically 40% of the selling price; distributers receive a 10% cut, leaving about 50% for the publisher. The publisher must distribute its profit between printing, marketing, and warehousing. Because of these constraints, publishers have created the "7x rule": A book must be listed for at least seven times more than the cost to print in order to be profitable. Amazon essentially eliminates these extra costs by removing the intermediaries between the author and consumer, enabling the company to keep prices lower than almost any retailer. In "Print on Demand and the Changing Face of Book Publishing," George Alexander writes "Amazon can discount most books because it pays the same amount of money to get them as physical stores do but has only a fraction of their costs." Bezos's tactic from the beginning was to drop book prices as low as possible in order to increase traffic on his website, thus increasing the purchase of Amazon's variety of other goods. Because of this method, consumers and competing retailers have developed a very strong opinion of the company. Jim Milliot sums up consumers' perspectives well in his article "Can Anyone Compete with Amazon?" by paraphrasing Peter Hildick-Smith, CEO of the Codex Group: "As has been well documented, Amazon is focused on driving prices as low as possible. The perception of Amazon as the cheapest place to buy books and its free shipping offers give the company a tremendous advantage over both online and physical book selling competitors." Because of these historically low prices, Amazon has developed an attractive reputation.

Bezos's pricing strategy has caused much disruption within the book-selling business, especially as Amazon's e-books have consistently commanded a large portion of the market. In Nicholas Clee's article "How I Learned to Stop Worrying and Love Amazon," Tim Godfray, the chief executive of the Booksellers Association, explains that booksellers find it difficult to compete against Amazon, which causes customers to have reduced book retailer choices. According to Maria Minsker in "Dynamic Pricing Gains Ground," an approach known as dynamic pricing is being adopted by retailers to compete with Amazon. This strategy, commonly adopted by Amazon's competition, entails investing in pricing intelligence software that adjusts product prices every ten minutes to be comparable to Amazon's. The fact that Amazon is pushing retailers to a state of paranoia further proves its dominance in the market.

Nifty Gadgets

Amazon's intensely low book prices are supported greatly by the innovations integrated into the company's website and delivery tactics, which have drawn consumers in droves and contributed to its success. Features such as "Search Inside the Book," which allows customers to look within a book without having to buy it, significantly contribute to the high traffic Amazon's website has attained. "1-Click" shopping, a strategy that is patented by Amazon, redefines convenience for the consumer, as customers' address and credit card information are saved to the website; "there's just you and the BUY button," explains Packer. Features such as these contribute to Bezos's overall attempt to create a shopping experience for consumers that no other retailer can provide. Former Amazon entertainment editor Tim Appelo, as quoted by Packer, explains that "'Jeff [Bezos] is trying to create a machine that assumes the shape of public demand.'" Shipping, a traditionally standard procedure, has also been touched by Bezos and his wand of innovation. AmazonPrime members receive their items a mere two days after purchase, as well as free shipping. This streamlined process is achieved through the company's distribution process. Amazon sets up warehouses in areas of low employment and hires workers by the hundreds. The scene within a warehouse is intense and often compared with the factory scene in Charlie Chaplain's *Modern Times.* "Pickers" within the warehouse are timed by computerized handsets as they speedily walk up to eleven miles per shift through a million-square-foot warehouse; some orders are expected to be collected within thirty-three seconds. This exhaustive process reportedly prompted ambulances to park outside an Amazon warehouse during a heat wave so that they could bus overheated and exhausted workers to emergency rooms. However, Bezos is not satisfied with these innovations: The thirteenth wealthiest man in the country has predicted that within five years, a drone delivery service will replace "the human factor" within the company's shipping process. Bezos and his seemingly never-ending bag of tricks attracted consumers in 1994 and continue to "wow" audiences over twenty years later.

In the wake of Amazon's success in the book-selling industry, book retailers of lesser size have felt extreme discomfort as the company dwarfs competitors. According to Wasserman in "The Amazon Effect," two decades ago, 4,000 independent bookstores existed in the United States; only about 1,900 remained as of 2012. The largest retailers, who were partially responsible for the decline in indie bookstores, have themselves not gone unscathed by Amazon's dominance: "Borders declared bankruptcy in 2011 . . . [Barnes & Noble] is nonetheless desperately trying to figure out ways to pay the mortgage on the considerable real estate occupied by its 1,332 stores across the nation," Wasserman elaborated. Amazon's significant hold on the book-selling industry is undeniable: The death of Borders proved its dominance, and the consistency of consumer traffic on Amazon.com continually confirms it. Whether Bezos intended for Amazon to practically engulf the industry or not, Amazon, through its unprecedented pricing and innovative features, consistently proves that it has no problems with causing waves in the book-selling trade.

E-novative Publishing

In the mind of the public, Amazon is currently recognized, and possibly idolized, for its territory in the e-book industry, which can be credited for a large portion of the company's success. To the average consumer, the invention of technologies such as the Kindle introduced them to an entirely new world of convenience. In 2007, as thirty-something moms sipped decaf cappuccinos while reading the latest Nicholas Sparks novel on their handheld screens, little did they know that in office suites in New York City, publishing executives were quickly growing gray over the battleground Amazon had just created out of the industry. And for the first time in the history of the industry, the Big Six had a gun pointed at them.

The traditional publishing model has been universally adhered to by publishing houses for decades. Before the digitalization boom, authors and their proposed titles were introduced in hardback and sold at a rather high price, because publishers needed to make some money out of the business. If that copy received good reviews and brought in appropriate sales, a paperback copy would then be published. The introduction of digital publishing, led by Amazon, threatened this format and the companies that adhered to it. Customers, who were accustomed to the sticker-shock associated with looking just above the barcode on the back of any book, obviously rejoiced in harmonious "hoorays" when Amazon promoted its Kindle through selling *New York Times* bestsellers at $9.99. Book publishers, not surprisingly, were less than thrilled with Amazon's grand entrance onto the publishing scene.

A precedent was set by Amazon's competitive pricing strategy, which resulted in readers' expecting their e-books to be cheap. In response to this, the Big Six teamed up with Apple to combat Amazon's growing dominance. The conglomerate took a swing at Amazon by adopting the "agency model" pricing strategy, in which publishers negotiated with retailers to set prices. Because Amazon's extremely low prices on e-books had consumers accustomed to discounted books, the goal of this endeavor was to increase the perceived value of e-books. Authorities in the United States and Europe charged the conglomerate with collusion and ordered five out of six of the publishing houses involved to pay over $160 million to American consumers in compensation for escalated prices. Amazon came out as the beneficiary of these squabbles; "Amazon, above the fray, was the victor in these cases . . . no authority is going to curb competitive aggression. The authorities are unconcerned about what share Amazon takes of the book market, provided book buyers continue to have choices," explains Clee. Though insiders within the publishing industry are crying foul in response to Amazon's low prices on e-books, the ultimate determining factor in Amazon's success is consumer response; so long as customers are satisfied with the company's colossal hold on the industry, authorities will not intervene.

Amazon's Reign: Not "The End" for Books?

The environment of reading has changed. In an industry comprised of traditionalists who professedly smell the innards of books to calm themselves, none would expect that a majority of its profits would come from e-book sales. Twenty years ago, when Jeff Bezos set out to revolutionize a trade that had been relatively unchanged for generations, no one could have predicted the far-reaching effects a little bald man with a dream could have on how an entire nation buys and reads books. Until Amazon, hot shots like Barnes & Noble and Borders were virtually untouchable, what with their enticing plush chairs and fresh coffee. Until Amazon, the Big Six sat comfortably on their hills, reigning over the industry with little fear of ever being chastised. Whether Bezos and his massive empire are the benevolent rescuers of an industry in desperate need of an update, or the malevolent force that threatens the realm of reading, there is no doubt that Amazon has forever changed the book trade. Through its unparalleled prices, novel features, and e-book revolution, Amazon has immensely altered the face of book sales and publishing. Though Bezos is feared and resented by many who relish the young girl who was captivated by the kingdom unlocked through a bookstore, perhaps Amazon did something the entire industry was too afraid to do: modernize what is held between hands so that future eyes can read what is between the covers.

Racism Is Like Spaghetti, But It Also Isn't

MARELLA GAYLA, Grade 12, Age 17. Marymount School of New York, New York, NY. Martha Erskine, *Educator*

I was pondering the irony of my school shortening Martin Luther King Jr. weekend by one day in favor of lengthening Thanksgiving break when I realized that my birthday was coming up on January 31st. It's not that I was shocked by how quickly seventeen had snuck up on me, how swiftly my youth is slipping from my hands and everything. Sixteen's been fun, but fully identifying with the protagonist of ABBA's "Dancing Queen" and watching R-rated movies without the company of an adult sounds one hell of a lot better.

The imminent celebration of my birth wasn't as striking as the realization that my birthday is one day before the start of Black History Month, the glorious 28 days when our nation pretends to be less racist than it actually is. I panicked, wondering if Black History Month was some sort of hibernation period or Lent for racists and that my birthday was some sort of field day for our nation's supremacists. Perhaps my birthday was secretly a day of saturated, uninhibited bigotry, a pre-hibernation feast or Mardi Gras of sorts before the fast. Perhaps racists flushed out 28 days' worth of slurs before the inundation of Martin Luther King Jr. remembrance tweets sent them into silence.

I'm kidding. Obviously I know that racism doesn't take any vacations. It's a year-round commitment, really; it just puts on a trench coat and glasses during the month of February. I figured that the first day of February and the last day of Slightly Racist Month #1 would most likely boast average quotients of ignorance, not too different from the rest of the year. I laughed to myself, anticipating the onslaught of age-old questions that next month would bring. *"Why isn't there White History Month? Or White Entertainment Television?"* Truly my favorite kind of questions. I enjoy answering them with a cup of tea by the fireplace, listening to the pitter-patter of white tears against my window. Nothing pleases me more than revealing The Big Secret: that such things do exist, but they can be hard to spot since they're cleverly disguised with names like *history class* or *television*.

And ah, how could I forget, "But aren't black people pretty racist to white people when they say we can't dance?" Well, to quote Black History Month heroine Rosa Parks: "No." At this point, a lot of Merriam-Webster aficionados like to pull out their dictionaries and say, "Well, hey, this says that racism is the belief that your race is superior to others, so black people actually can be pretty racist to white people." To that I say, "Well, if you're looking at a book probably written by white men to understand racism, that's pretty problematic."

This brings me to the title of this blog post: Racism Is Sort of Like Spaghetti, But It Also Isn't. I'll be the first to admit that racism is far from comforting and delicious, but the metaphor does work on some level. If you looked up the definition of spaghetti in the dictionary, you would probably get something like, "pasta made in long, slender, solid strings" or "an Italian dish consisting largely of this, typically with a sauce." Does this accurately describe your experience of eating spaghetti? I'll guess that it doesn't. Similarly, a two-line dictionary definition of racism can hardly compete with the decades (even centuries) of subjugation and discrimination that people of color have faced. I speak from the point of view of an Asian-American (our month is in May; racists, prepare yourselves accordingly), and even if it isn't my heritage's official month, I'm pretty damn tired of people trying to convince me that racism can be summarized by Merriam-Webster or Oxford.

If you ever find yourself trying to explain a pervasive social plague such as racism using a dictionary, I urge you to ask yourself if "pasta made in long, slender, solid strings" is the best way to explain your experience of eating spaghetti. If it is, then you, my friend, have been eating really shitty spaghetti.

A Defector and Family's Guide to the Aftermath of Defection from North Korea

OLIVIA DABICH, Grade 11, Age 16. Marshall High School, Falls Church, VA. Martha Noone, *Educator*

Part 1 (The Commercial)

Are you experiencing the following signs?
- feeling of abandonment
- confusion
- disgrace
- lack of closure
- getting tortured by your own government
- getting sent to a gulag (and having three generations of your family stay there)

Or are you experiencing:
- some feelings of relief (but mostly guilt)
- trouble adjusting to capitalism, free speech (basically all human rights)
- ghost limb sensation

If you answered "yes" to any of these, chances are that you are a defector or family member of a defector and are experiencing the aftermath of defection from North Korea. For more information on this condition, please read the following guide.

Part 2 (The Guide)

Generation 1 (North Korea)

When they tell you that your sister has defected, denounce her—wear your best Kim Il Sung lapel pin, the one you bought last "Day of the Shining Star," and with eyes wide and unbelieving, tell them that you had no idea about the plan, and that she was always the rotten one in the family (though on the inside, you are holding hands with her, thirteen and sixteen caught in the dappled light of perpetual summer). They will take you and your family anyway, but perhaps you will get sent to Camp 14 instead of Camp 18, a better kind of hell.

Generation 1 (America)

You wear guilt like a straitjacket. A week ago, you sat at your family's dinner table in North Korea, bent, like a perpetual apology. Once, a toothless peasant woman read your lifelines like a pack of tarot cards, telling you that you would live a long life. She did not say anything to your sister right next to you. America is a land of talk shows and therapists, of mending and feeling, of trying to remember and heal, but for you, guilt ticks inside of you like a maddening metronome until all you can see is regret. Perhaps, the best thing to do is to forget.

Generation 2 (gulag, North Korea)

Hunger is the only tattered dress you have ever worn—it does not fit you well. On your fifth birthday, you watched a man get shot, watched him fall to the ground like a ragdoll, and felt nothing. Your mother disappeared with a prison guard and never came back. He came back, however, and stole another woman. Your life can best be explained as a clock, something thought to move forward and change, but really just a circle, a perpetual loop. The best thing to do is survive.

Generation 2 (America)
You will hear about your mother's past life in the form of a fairytale, an allegory. Your mother is obsessed with the process of baking, of making something whole through a chemical process that cannot be undone. At night, she shakes loose her composed façade and drifts back into her past life in North Korea, crying out the names of ghosts into the implacable darkness. The darkness replies, sputtering with broken AM radio static. You can never bring back the dead.

Generation 3 (gulag, North Korea)
This is what you know—a barbed-wire fence, guards (everywhere), skeletally thin people, and ash. Ash in the clouds, ash in the ground, ash in the eyes of everyone you meet. It was said once that your ancestors lived in the place beyond the fence. And you, a sacrificial lamb, a phoenix, the last generation for and from the ash—survive.

Generation 3 (America)
The best kinds of horror stories are the ones that seem the least real. It was said once that your grandmother defected from North Korea and abandoned her family there. In America, the land of life, liberty, and the pursuit of happiness, this place of barbed-wire fences and people with paper-skin stretched over sallow-winged bones seems so distant. Be thankful, and embrace opportunity.

Was it worth it?

Chuck Taylors

KINGSLEY-WYNN UKUKU, Grade 10, Age 15. Goose Creek High School, Goose Creek, SC. Nick Geary, *Educator*

My first kiss was stolen by a boy with beer breath and weird shoes. We met during summer at the age of eight on a chipped porch. The smell of cut grass and apple pie swirled in front of my nose when Father, Mother, and I knocked on their door.

"Welcome, neighbors," my mother said. I remember the boy's mom was wearing a dress, though I can't recall the color. She smiled sweetly and laughed at the gap between my front teeth when I smiled back. She accepted our pie graciously. "I'm Lilian, this is my husband, Carl," my mother said.

"Annabeth," she replied. "Mike's at work, but my son Jack— Jackson, be polite, say hello!"

"Hi," mumbled a voice behind the dress. It was the first time I saw him, and in my heart, even at such a young age, I knew. He cowered behind his mother, his only visible characteristics being his shining blue eyes and the cute brown hair that flopped into them. Well, that and his shoes. One was red, the other blue.

"This here's our beautiful Sophie," my mother bragged.

Annabeth tried to shake her son away. "Say hello to Sophie, Jack."

"But she's a girl."

"Jack!" My heart's thudding dulled down and the smile on my face was replaced with a scowl.

"Nice shoes," I sneered. Jackson frowned, walked toward me, and tugged on one of my blonde pigtails, hard.

From that moment on, Jackson's eyes no longer shined, and his hair wasn't cute. The only thing he had going for him was the unique ability to make something out of a poor family who couldn't even afford him nice shoes.

Despite our mutual hate for one another, our parents became best friends. There was never a summer night that I wasn't lulled to sleep by the sound of the TV down the hall, or the dull conversations our parents had about sports or the weather. His family liked to visit because our TV was in color, and we had a patio out back where our fathers sat and drank beer.

When we were thirteen—Jackson's shoes were black and yellow that day—we went through the struggle of trying to steal one.

"Just distract them," Jackson told me, as if it were obvious.

"No. I'm not getting in trouble just because you wanna try some alcohol. My mother will have my behind if we get caught."

"Then don't get caught." He sauntered onto the patio, confident and cocky. I glared as he made his way to the cooler and hurried after him, standing in front of our fathers.

"Hey, Little Sophie." Mr. Mike smiled up at me from the lawn chair. I smoothed out my dress and rocked on my heels.

"Mr. Michael—"

"What do you need from us today?" Jackson slyly pulled open the cooler and dug inside.

"Just need to ask a question."

"Well, go right on ahead."

"Where does Jackson get his shoes?" Jackson's head popped

up from behind the lid of the cooler and he eyed me accusingly. I ignored him.

"Sophie!" my father scolded.

"I just wanna know why they never match!"

Mr. Mike threw a hand toward my father, signaling that it was okay.

"Oh, Jack's been doing that since he was a boy. We've tried to make him stop, but you know how it is. Can't teach an old pony new tricks."

"I think it's 'old dog,' sir." My father gave me a mean glare. Jackson was standing by the door now, gesturing for me to get out. "Sorry, that was it."

I rushed away, and Jackson and I sat in the hall out of everyone's line of sight since we weren't allowed alone in my room. He took a sip, puckered his lips, and then passed it to me.

"Ugh," I whispered after I swigged. "Tastes like pee."

"Yeah, and how'd you know?" he snapped. It was the same routine every day they came over all summer. He'd convince me to help, I'd distract our fathers, he'd steal only one beer, and I'd complain to him about it for the rest of the night. It was against the rules, and it stomped on my nerves, but I never stopped.

No, it was Jackson who gave up on stealing the beer once we were sixteen. That was the year that his family stopped visiting, and Mr. Mike left for work but never came back.

He died in an accident, but I was always too scared to ask how it happened. Jackson didn't come out of his room that summer. Sometimes I'd sneak to him at night, tapping on his window angrily.

"Jackson!" I'd whisper. "Come out! Aren't you going to church?" or "Don't you know what time it is?" sometimes even "Fine, I never liked talking to you anyways."

We didn't speak much then. In fact, in those three months, we'd only talked at the funeral. That day Jackson's shoes were black, the both of them. I watched him all the way to my seat in the pew, and he glanced at me only once. He left halfway through the service and, after a few moments, I followed him.

I found him behind the church, a case of beer at his side and the familiar scowl on his face. I didn't say anything. I stood beside him. He removed the bottle from his lips and held it toward me, silently asking if I wanted some. I didn't, I still hated the taste, but I drank it anyways. I gave it back to him and looked down at my feet.

"You like my shoes?" I asked, bumping the toe of my white one against the black. I looked up at him and for the first time in a long time those blue eyes shined again. Then he leaned forward and stole my first kiss.

Never Become a Writer

AMELIA VAN DONSEL, Grade 10, Age 15. Waltham Senior High
School, Waltham, MA. Jeanette Amiano, *Educator*

You'll want someone exotic, and marry a Romanian. He'll tell
you to dye your hair and you'll do it, then make chewing on its
multicolored strands a habit. You'll kiss him once and say he
tastes like wine. Wine, no? he'll say with a grin. Only gentlemen
drink wine. You'll leave him because you won't like clichés.

You'll find a shadow behind a counter (because that's the
only way to describe him). You'll watch him clashing silverware
around in drawers like cold piles of bones, and he'll give you a
free slice of key-lime pie and say it's the best in the state. You'll
lick up its tanginess on the prongs of your fork and decide that
it's not, but you won't pull away from his eyes that will remind
you of your favorite crayon. Then he'll look you up and down
and say, another? You'll decide to love him because anyone
worth loving is worth a free slice of key-lime pie. You'll make
him kiss you even when he doesn't want to by threatening to
write down all of him, and then he'll press his lips to yours right
there under the spidered glint of the sun's smothering smolder.

It'll be two years, and you'll marry that shadow. (He'll know
all about what you do by then.) He'll know that you pick away

at life's cadaver, which has long since gone stiff and cold. That you wade through the platitudes and search its chalk skeleton anyway, hunting for the similes and metaphors that glint like chipped glass. You'll tell him that you'll stop when you can build a world, but you won't tell him that you've already made one. He'll let you. He won't be able to watch when you're starved of words at 2:00 am. He'll yell at you because you were defining love in your sleep, and you'll write an angry poem on a napkin in a diner about how you don't care. You'll lie. And you'll try not to care.

But you will write down all of him until the bump on your middle finger bulges. From his rusted hair to his eyes that will shine like oil to his honey-dipped lips to his hands too loose for his body; and soon you'll hate every word because you'll realize that you like the paper version of him better than the real thing. You are going to write about those white, jingling shells on the beach because they will remind you of keys in his pocket, about those angles of geese in the sky that shift and cross effortlessly because they will remind you of his fingers. You'll read about the billions of stars and planets to him on the spiky, stiff grass in the dark until he says he feels so crowded he'll suffocate, and you say you feel so endless you'll burst. You'll be unable to stop yourself from reaching into his drawers and beneath his bed and reading his poetry. It will be bad, but you won't say so (he's not the writer, after all). It'll be the kind that compares eyes to stars, wishes to stones. You won't mind.

There will be times when you have to write; when you screw up bad with him, when you're dry of idioms and surrounded by pages of nothing to say, when you cut off all your hair and cry for a day, when your skin wrinkles, but he says he doesn't care because his is retreating too; you'll write about it. His shoulders will curl with age, and you'll make him wear a blanket around the house even though he'll say he's not cold. Years will follow each other as quickly as days, and you'll read the vomitings of dead poets to him until he sleeps at the sound of your heart, until the dead night drops down at its knees, and until the sun torches the leaves key-lime. You'll hand I-love-yous across glacial sheets that feel like newspaper, and he'll shakily toss it back. You won't want to, but you'll write for his voice, which will turn husky with drought, for his loose, trembling hands that will turn to roots, for his face full of similes, and for his quiet that will always be there like a shadow.

And you'll let it all dribble out of you until you're empty and aching for more, the crook of your elbow no longer itching, your neck softened, released by the icy shot of words. It will hurt. More than any simile can describe. And you won't be able to stop.

Marianne

LIZZY LEMIEUX, Grade 10, Age 16. Gorham High School, Gorham, ME.
Kerry Herlihy and Lucinda Stein, *Educators*

This is Brooklyn and these are the '70s. They're full up with
the elbows of street corners and the elbows of those who in-
habit them, actors, artists, and whores. It brims with smog like
a pot boiling over, and in the summertime, the artists stick to
themselves while the whores stick to strangers. It is not so bad.
The old Jewish men pray to God here, and their wives plan
weddings in stuffy apartments. It smells of sweat and kugel,
and when the bridge is filled with cars in hot afternoons, the
heat makes it seem like it sways. Behind the fence posts of people standing on the street corners are buildings where people
live and die, and it happens softly and inconspicuously. Brooklyn does not call them tragedies. Brooklyn calls them by name.
Brooklyn calls him Russell, and he calls Brooklyn home.

In this little, dingy apartment, he is not thinking of Brooklyn. He is thinking of a girl who calls herself Marianne and
looks small and slender and bitter. She wears her mouth and
necklaces the same way, hanging in curves across her pink
skin. When she brings strangers home, they leave her wads of
cash in a jar on her dresser, and when she talks to Brooklyn

she calls it the name of mutts who beg for scraps and rain with hanging jowls: bitch. In turn, Brooklyn spits it back, and it sounds sour and cold in the mouths of men with thick accents and canker sores.

"Bitch," Brooklyn says, and Marianne sways faster and warmer on her street corner and pretends she does not hear.

Marianne rises from the mess of the bed, drapes herself in the sheet, and looks at the way her leg is outlined by the fabric. Russell sees it as a prayer shawl and prays she will let it drop to the ground.

His shawl belonged to his grandfather, who still lives back in the Old Country that his mother is always telling him about in her strange way, a mix of Yiddish and English weaving itself together in half-hearted assimilation. That girl, Rita, had been there when he put it on, that girl, Rita, had watched it slip again and again from his shoulders that had yet to take the shape of a man's.

That girl, Rita, had fit so well into the row of mothers and grandmothers who grew fatter as they progressed with age, but she, at the base of the row, had been slender. She had pressed the blue fabric of her dress to her legs the same way Marianne presses the sheet to skin, and that girl, Rita, had been the one to watch him pray, rocking back and forth and murmuring to himself. She'd had a drink with him on the patio outside the shul, their purple knees knocking together, blistery colored from the cold.

That girl, Rita, makes him dinner and sleeps on the left side of their queen bed. He should get back.

"I should get back," he says, hitching his pants to his hips.

"Okay."

"Rita's making stew for dinner."

Marianne faces him from where he stands, leaning against

the bathroom door frame.

"Go home, Russell," she says.

He gets up. He ties his shoelaces, smoothes his hair in the mirror.

"Leave the money," she calls out.

He fishes the cash from his pockets and catches a cab home.

They live on the fourth floor. It's cramped, and Rita likes to forget to sweep, but she always makes the table with their wedding dishes, which are brown and sturdy and secondhand.

"Did you have a good day?" she asks from across the place settings, looking like his mother with her hair pulled back like that, all wispy and soft.

He nods. "How are you?"

He watches her move, his eyes on her belly, which seems as if it has grown into itself.

"I'm good, Russell," she sighs quietly. She looks at his jaw.

"We should talk."

"Russell, please . . ."

They watch each other. She's lost weight. He might be losing his hair.

He clears away his plate. "My mother wants to have us over for Shabbos." He turns on the faucet, lets the sink fill up with hot bubbles.

"We should go. Will your sister be there?"

He shrugs. "Yeah, but I'm just not ready yet, you know?"

"I know," Rita breathes.

The bed they share was a wedding gift. Rita likes to fold back the blankets and the duvet in layers like a cake so it looks like they're still staying in that honeymoon hotel on the waterfront. When it gets dark, she peels it back and sits on the edge of the mattress, massaging cream into her palms and in the dry places between her fingers. Russell takes off his big, barred, glasses, sets them down, and leans back against the headboard.

The room feels emptier than when they first moved in. They hadn't been the only ones expecting, the room was waiting with them.

"I didn't think you'd come home," she laughs, closing the tin of lotion.

"That's not me, Rita," Russell says.

She stops laughing. "I know."

"I'm looking for work."

She pats her hands together so they make a soft noise and then she mimics him, leaning against the headboard. "I know." She presses her hand into his. He takes it even though it's still wet from lotion. She leans in to kiss him.

"Rita," he says. She flicks off the light.

Marianne does not sleep the same way Russell does. She presses her face into the pillows, forgets everything she can about him, from the pale skin on his calves that she touches tenderly when he watches her, to the pimples on his cheek, red and raw. He does everything he can to recreate her, even though she is not particularly beautiful. When he wakes up, maybe he'll look over and Marianne will be the one with her skinny body covered up by the duvet, her thin hair in knots against the bed.

In the morning, he goes back to Marianne. When they rise from the tangle of sheets that canopies over their bodies, Russell thinks about his last wedding, mostly the chuppah, and he draws himself away from Marianne's pearly skin, thinking of his sister Eileen.

It was her wedding. Her groom was neat and polished. At the synagogue, the building filled with Yiddish. The People sat in clustered rows and filtered in late through skinny doors in fat groups. Russell was fifteen and playing by running his fingers over the edges of wine glasses so they screeched and hummed and made noises he mimicked, whoops and hollers and cries. The women were flustered and flying, parakeets with shawls that gathered around their wide hips. His mother, in her thin high heels, ran back and forth from the kitchen, clicking across the tile, to where his sister was dressing, fixing her makeup in a compact. Between her fingers she pinched the rolls of her stomach and watched herself sour. She always went hungry before she had to wear a dress.

Eileen pulled the veil over her eyes and examined the way it softened her jaw like a Monet.

"Bubeleh, wish your sister luck!" hissed a woman called Lilian. She pinched his cheek affectionately, and he dipped away, dipping like her dress, which burrowed into her cleavage. He nodded.

Now he wishes that he remembered how Lilian looked. She was exotic, the only Jew he knew with dark skin, from Colombia, and though she did not know Hebrew or Yiddish, she could babysit for Hispanic boys with chubby faces and legs and arms. But they all faded together, Eileen and Lilian and Rita and his mother, and now, Marianne. He put them together like a Picasso until they were indecipherable, and now he wishes he wasn't in love with any of them, let alone all of them.

"Good luck," he said to Eileen, and she smiled, pulling him to her in a hug that smelled of lilac and hairspray. When Eileen talked to Brooklyn, she called it something syrupy, sweetheart or love. Russell had worried that when her fiancé carried her over the threshold of their new apartment, she would rid herself of him, turned into a mirror image of their mother, complete with the love of the Old Country and matzoh ball soup.

So when she stood under the chuppah of white silk, which

still is the most expensive thing the family has owned, she looked adoring and kind and impossibly far away, like she was made of glass, white from her buckled throat to her swooping ankles, fragile and breakable.

Marianne is unbreakable and not made of glass. She, too, has swooping ankles with the bone jutting out, but her legs are blotchy and bloated and she does not stare into his eyes like Eileen looked at Danny. Instead, she watches herself as she moves and is careful to put on airs even undressed. If she were not poor and naked, she could pass as high class. When Russell thinks of Marianne, which he does when he doesn't want to think of Rita, he thinks of her in Lilian's dress with the dipping cut, gaudy pearls weighing down her neck until it kinks like a garden hose. He doesn't think of her without her clothing.

"Are you going to get up?" Marianne asks, watching him stare at the ceiling vacantly, her lips taut.

He nods, stands, and deposits the money on her dresser. When he reaches for the door knob, he clenches it tightly until his knuckles go white. The women in his life always had something to say about the way he held things, the way he slumped and held himself bent, as if from the rain that washed Brooklyn into the gutters. His mother had tried to soothe him with teas and homeopathy.

"It makes you look so angry," she'd complained, her hands thrust into the suds of the sink. "You should stand like your father does! Shoulders back, chest out, eyes straight ahead . . . there you go!" His mother had always tried to make him elegant. She said that in the shtetl, where their people were busy living and dying, the young people would dance to fiddles played with cat gut bows, and their bodies would bend like light through glass. He should go dancing more.

His girlfriends, too, in turn had said something in their own unique way. Not that any of them were unique, they were everyone's typical cast of high school crushes, but each fell into different categories of normal and spoke with contrasting lilts.

Gentle Margaret, with her big eyes like baseball bobble-heads, had run her white fingers over his until he unclenched them and looked up at her. "I wish you wouldn't do that," she sighed, "it makes you look so angry all the time."

But that hadn't stopped him when Josie came around, and he held doors open for her and lost the circulation in his fingers. "Jesus!" she'd cried, tossing back her ruddy hair and looking at his tie-dye skin. "You need to unwind! You're like the Hulk, Russell."

When Laura, the last girl before Rita, tried to stop him, she squawked out commands with her beaky nose bobbing up and down. "Stop holding things like that! You look like a murderer. My parents will be so nervous if you show up for dinner looking like this." They had hated him when he'd showed up like that, looming, encasing Laura's petite shadow. She had dumped him on the stoop of their apartment and feigned regret.

When he and Rita had gone out at first, she had run her thumb across his. "Ease up, sweet," she'd hummed, popping a piece of bubblegum against the roof of her mouth, "I hate it when you can't relax, it makes me nervous." She had leaned into his chest, and he had felt her heartbeat and wondered if he loved her.

Marianne doesn't care how he holds his hands or his back, and for a moment he says to himself that he loved her because of that. He stands abruptly, throwing himself off balance and teetering back and forth as if praying.

"My mom invited me . . ." he starts.

Marianne stands and shakes her head. "Don't tell me about

your life, okay?"

He nods. "Okay."

New Yorkers have a thing about tipping. He should probably leave Marianne a tip on the dresser, but he doesn't. He just goes home. When the yellow taxi lets him out, he sees Rita standing in front of their building, wringing her hands like a dishcloth. He doesn't see her much on the sidewalks. Rita has a different name for Brooklyn, and it's not home or bitch; to her, it's just Brooklyn. Russell thinks she looks as if she might float away, back to wherever she came from.

"Is everything okay?"

She smiles up at him. "Yeah. I'm going to your mother's for Shabbos."

He frowns. "Why?"

"I want to see Eileen. I want to see *people*, Russell," she says. "You've been gone a lot, you know. So I'm going to go, and I'll say you're sick and that you're sorry you can't be there, but come on, it's so hot in there. I'm tired."

His hands are fists. "Please, come back inside. I'm sorry. We can turn on the fan." He takes the door handle firmly, spoons her back with the crook of his arm and shepherds her back inside. "Come on, sweetheart. Why don't you call your friends from upstate? You can meet up in the city, yeah?"

She backs away.

"Please, come on, let's go upstairs . . ." Russell pleads.

She shakes her head. "Why does it matter?"

He breathes in. "I never got a chance to tell her, Rita. I called. I talked to her on the phone, but Jesus, I just didn't get a chance to tell her."

"And?"

"And I'm not ready to."

"Fine, but I am," Rita says, picking at her fingernails and

making them tick together. She doesn't look down, just lets them tick. "It was my baby too and I'm sorry, but I'm going to go have dinner with your mother. I'm going to go tell her, and you are just going to have to be a man about this."

That baby had been theirs. He had picked out names. She had hated them. Eileen had knitted them a blanket and his mother had bought them a crib. The Salvation Army would thank them for it.

Another taxi pulls up to the curb and Rita sits in the back, her hands folded in her lap.

"Rita," Russell says, because he can't think of anything.

"It's okay."

He leans against the wall of their apartment and closes his eyes so he doesn't have to watch her close the door and drive off. She keeps saying it will be okay.

It was a long time before he went inside, and it was a long time before he went to bed. He wasn't waiting up for her, he wasn't waiting up for anyone, but he was waiting.

There was nothing that felt safe or kind. Sometimes there was Marianne, but mostly there was just Rita, and there was just Russell. She left and he stayed, his body cradled in Brooklyn.

That's How Summer Passed

SOPHIE GLESSNER, Grade 11, Age 17. Sheyenne High School, West Fargo, ND. Marci Glessner, *Educator*

"Stop." Tucker's voice cuts through the miles of thick silence, commanding even as a whisper.

The old truck whines as it's maneuvered onto an overgrown back road, kicking up dust that hasn't been disturbed in years. The engine makes an awful crunching sound as Sean throws it into park, but he ignores it in favor of side-eyeing the boy in the passenger seat. "Why are we stopping?"

Tucker lets his head fall back against the cracked leather seat, digging in the deep pockets of his—Sean's, actually—hoodie for something. "It felt right." He lets out a soft hum of approval as he pulls out a pack of cigarettes.

"Don't smoke in my car," Sean says as Tucker cranks the window down a few inches, but there's no real venom behind it. They both know he's not gonna do anything about it, he's never done anything about it.

The car's not even that important to him. ("What're you looking for, son?" A sleazy car salesman, with a weird amount of sweat on his upper lip, asks.

Sean feels his lip split open again as he answers, tries to ignore the familiar taste of blood in his mouth. "Anything that'll get me out of here.") Maybe the car's a little important to him. He spent his college money on the piece of shit.

He watches Tucker's brow furrow in concentration as he holds the cigarette between his teeth and sparks his old lighter with gloved fingers. Tucker shivers, and the smoke follows the motion, wavering as it slips out of the crack between window and car frame.

Sometimes, when they've been on the road for a few days and money is short, they run out of cigarettes. That's when Tucker's hands get shaky and he doesn't sleep and he has headaches so bad he yells without meaning to. That's when Sean begs him to quit, to get through this now so the pain doesn't come back again.

And the answer is always the same. "Maybe when we settle down." He offers the same lazy grin with it, a package deal. "Maybe when this shitstorm *you* kicked up finally settles down." And it's another guilt-edged knife straight to the heart.

"Come on, Tuck, why are we stopped?" Sean shakes his hands as he waits for an answer, trying to get the blood flowing through his fingers again, spread some warmth where it wasn't retained by the worn leather of his gloves. "We're in the middle of nowhere."

"The sun's setting."

"The sun sets every night." (The sun set that night. When the truck rumbled to a stop outside the group home, when Sean pushed his way through the sea of grubby children under ten and finally bumped chest-to-chest with Tucker.

"Get your coat." His voice is nothing. His voice is a black hole with a gaping maw, hungry and hungry and never satisfied.

There's a hand under his chin, slender fingers skimming along the edge of his bruised cheekbone, angry dark eyes staring into his. "Did he hit you again?"

"Get your coat," Sean repeats, shaking his head minutely. Not here, not here, never here. "We're leaving.")

"Tonight's sunset is different." Those elegant fingers stumble over something unseen, recalibrate, and tap the end of the cigarette to let the ash spill onto the frosted gravel. "Trust me."

The thick silence returns like a fog through the front of the car, coating the inside of Sean's throat and turning his lips to rubber. The smoke continues to waft its way into the cold night air until Tucker snuffs it out against a wrinkled tissue. He frowns at it before crumpling the tissue in his palm and shoving it into his deep pockets.

Sean leans forward. "You're not gonna throw it out the window?"

The door creaks as Tucker rolls the window back up. "Bad for the environment."

"So you *do* listen to me."

"Only when it's something you say twelve times a day." Another lazy smirk crosses his face as he slides his hand across the center console to intertwine their fingers. Their hands lie there, resting just under the weak green light of the car clock, interlaced so you could count: knuckle, knuckle, stray green thread, knuckle, knuckle, knuckle, gray thread. "Watch the sunset with me, Callaghan."

"You sure that's all you wanna do?"

Tucker laughs, and it's happy for once, floating up and filling the space between them, leaving them both too scared to speak lest they pop the fragile bubble. The moment breaks when Tucker runs his free hand through his dark hair, shakes it down into his eyes. "Maybe a little more. We could make out."

Sean reaches out to push at Tucker's chest, unable to stop

the blush from rising under his cheeks when his elbow hits the steering wheel and triggers the car horn. "I'm not making out with you if your breath smells like that."

"Fine." He drops Sean's hand and turns to dig through the plastic bags in the back. "Where's the gum?" (The fluorescent light buzzes and flickers above his head as Sean squeaks the cart across the tile flooring of the 24/7 grocery. Tucker slides around the corner and empties the load in his arms into the cart. "That's the cereal and the beef jerky. We need anything else?"

"I think that's everything." Tucker kicks at the wheels of the cart, Sean tries to run over his feet as they make their way out of the aisle.

As Sean transfers the few boxes onto the conveyor belt at the self-checkout, Tucker throws three packs of "extra fresh!" spearmint gum on top of the saltine crackers.)

The sharp smell of mint permeates the air as Tucker pops a bubble with a loud crack and grabs Sean's hand again. "Watch," he says around the wad in his cheek. "It's going down."

So they do. The sun begins to slip below the horizon, split by the reaching, spindly branches of the trees. Pale pink clouds disappear as soon as they appear, and the blue shade of the sky deepens with every passing second. The corona flares at the edge of the earth and fades, letting the royal dark descend.

"You happy now?"

Yes. Tucker wants to shout. *Yes, yes, yes. I am so happy.* But Sean can't see himself, and he doesn't know. He doesn't know it was the last summer sun sliding away. He can't see the way the last rays caught the blonde in his hair and the gold in his eyes, the last bit of light shining against his cheekbone. So he settles with a quiet hum. "Yes."

"Even though we didn't make out?"

He reaches over to take Sean's hand again. "Even though we didn't make out."

The grin that splits Sean's face is brighter than the sun and it makes the whole damn thing worth it. *It's you, it's you, it's always been you*, is what the beat of Tucker's heart says. But he knows. He might pull his hand away so he can switch gears and back out onto the interstate, but he still knows. He's always known.

"Hey," Sean says, as the tell-tale creaking of the window rolling down sounds under the crunch of tires on gravel. "Don't smoke in my car."

Islands

RACHEL PAGE, Grade 11, Age 16. Woodrow Wilson Senior High School, Washington, D.C. Kathy Crutcher, *Educator*

In the fifth week of melting, our town was split into eighteenths. The first crack appeared in the yard between the houses of the Millers and the Riveras. There was not enough time for them to say goodbye, or even to return the guinea pig that Andrew Miller had been taking care of while Manuel Rivera was away at boarding school. As the house dislodged itself, we could see the Rivera children, all six of them crowded in the wide mouth of the porthole window, their brown faces staring out at the peeling red of the Millers' front door as it got smaller and smaller until finally it was no more than a dot on the horizon and their faces were periods at the ends of sentences, so far off we had to squint to remind ourselves they were really still there.

The subsequent cracks appeared more slowly. In the following weeks, the houses separated and floated away from each other one by one—the Youngs, the Littletons, the McCarthys, the Garcias. We watched all of them disappear, tracking their movements on maps we had bought long ago but never thought we would have to use. Some of us began to tell stories: Isabel

Young and Richard Littleton had been having a covert affair for years, and when the first small hole emerged between their two houses, they stood on opposite ends of it for days, neither of them willing to cross over nor to look away from the other, lest that second be the second that the ice cracked for good. None of us have seen the Youngs or the Littletons for months, and none of us can say whether the stories are true, but no one can deny the way they looked at each other when waiting in line for the bank, or that time their hands touched over the grapes in the grocery store, and neither one of them pulled away.

At the beginning, we admit, it was almost beautiful. The quiet of the clink of dishes on the table as we walked down the stairs for breakfast, the simplicity of living only for our-selves. Our husbands made pancakes every morning and beef brisket every night until we could see the open-mouth circles and fibers when we closed our eyes. The sun, when it rises on the dark map of water, makes patterns that look like red fish. We laid on our backs at night and held hands and stared up at stars that seemed as though they would never end. It was beautiful for fifteen weeks and six days, to be alone and happy and indulgent in the small togetherness of our house-islands.

In the sixteenth week we began to want. Isabel Young want-ed coffee, which had run out two weeks ago, sniffed at the last dusty specks in the metal container when her husband wasn't in the kitchen as if it was a drug. Alicia Rivera wanted Manu-el's guinea pig back. Eliza James wanted to jump into the blue of the water and swim away. Abigail Miller wanted new books. Richard Littleton wanted Isabel Young. The things we wanted lined themselves up like floes in the emptiness outside our small icebergs. They drifted through the corners of our eyes; they appeared where we least expected them, in the tarnished brass of the doorknob or the rough bristles of a used tooth-brush. Conversation grew more difficult. We found that the words between us had been used up, obscured by the wants that gripped us like ice in the center of our chests. We lived instead for the times when we could talk to inhabitants of a different island, hear in their voices the whispers of things we could never have.

It has been six months now, and we can talk to each other only in snippets, yelled through rolled-up newspapers and dusty megaphones across an ever-widening gap of sea and green ice. We chart the passing of our separate icebergs like ships in the night. A quarter mile is cause for celebration—the whole family is called outside, thin black l's against the white of snow that flicker like mirages when they wave. Distances of forty feet or less are rare and calculated with mathematical precision. There's usually only an hour to talk, enough time to send the necessary news down the line: *Anna Martin is sick; Do you have any milk? We've run out of ours; Have you seen the Riveras?* Words are hard, chosen for which will take the least effort. Our chests hurt and our stores of dry cereal are running out, and so *Do you have any supplies?* becomes *Any supplies?* becomes *Supplies?* until hand waving must suffice, our own invented form of sign language.

A few weeks ago, Isabel Young gave birth to a baby boy. We heard it from the McCarthys, or maybe it was the Andersons. They say that he came out of her mouth one morning as she bent over her cereal bowl, no blood, only a small gush of water like melted ice. We have never heard of babies being born in this way. There are many things we have never heard of, in our closed-off islands of four walls and peeling-paint shutters. We feel the words we cannot say build themselves up inside of us, words that have no language, and we can almost understand how it is possible for this heaviness to find life in the beating of our hearts and the pulsing of our blood, to become something greater than we are. We imagine the feeling of opening our mouths and speaking out a son.

We do not know why, but Isabel Young's son becomes our obsession. We think about him as we lie in bed with our husbands, as we try to force clothes onto our own children, who have begun to walk around naked. They say that they must be closer to the ice, that we are older and do not understand, and we think of running our fingers over a smooth soft head and whispering stories of before to a child who can still be our own. He is here, always, with us. When we pass a neighboring iceberg, the only news we care about is stories of the baby— what he eats, how he sleeps, the sound of his laugh. We begin to hoard them. We hide our maps and charts so that we are the only ones in our family who know when we will pass; we tiptoe outside at midnight to call questions across a lonely sea. We pick and choose what to pass on to others. When he says his first word, we keep it to ourselves. We tell the others we pass that we've heard nothing, that perhaps he's a late bloomer, that our children didn't start talking until they were ten months old, or eleven, or twelve. When we're alone, we savor the sound of it on our tongue and know that we are the only ones who can know the beauty of the first thing he has given to the world.

Our children begin to stop eating. We push foods onto their plates and plead for them to swallow, but they spit it out when they think we're not looking. There is no dinnertime conversation. In the evenings we step out onto the porch to find them kneeling by the side of the house, shoveling snow into their mouths as though they will never eat again. Their bare skin is pink with cold, but they are too large to be babies. They sleep outside on the ice, and we see the way they press their ears to the frozen ground, as though it is telling them something that we cannot. We wonder if Isabel Young's son has started to eat solid food.

It is difficult to wake up or draw the curtains or move around the house without thinking of Isabel Young. We fill our rooms with babies. We collect our children's old baby dolls and give them special seats next to us at the table, or on the mantle, or looking out at us from the windowsill. The plastic hands fit perfectly on the rims of our children's empty plates at dinner time, which they have stopped attending. Outside we make gardens of ice babies, round and perfectly smooth. We mold them until our hands are numb and we can no longer feel the tips of our fingers. At sunrise, the light that shines through them is like a halo. They are more than alive.

Our husbands complain when we slide into bed next to them so late that the ice outside has already begun to glisten a morning rosy pink. They pull away from us. They tell us we are so cold they do not know us anymore, and we do not know what to say. We lie on top of the blankets so that all we can feel is the outline of a leg, the slight dip of a foot. This is good, we tell ourselves, it is good to have this space between us like sea between icebergs, dark and impersonal and inviting. When we can't sleep, we stand to look out the window at our children, who sleep naked on the snow. They curl themselves in almost the same positions as the ice babies, hands tucked over heads or under chins like statues, as if each is becoming the other.

In the sixth hour of the seventh day of the twelfth month, our children walk into the ocean. They do not look back. We watch them from our windows, parting the curtains with numb fingers, and do not think to tell them to stop. They are so small and their skin almost translucent, as if they, too, have become ice. There is no splash.

We are sure that there is some explanation for what they have done. We search for messages in the snow, written with the tip of a toe or a crooked finger. We climb onto the roofs of our houses to get a different vantage point—perhaps it is a word so big that we cannot see it from the ground. But all we see is the round teardrops of our ice babies' heads, which look oddly small and misshapen from above. When we look out over the sea, there is nothing but darkness, not even the crowns of our children's heads bobbing in the waves as we had somehow imagined.

Our husbands wake up and make us breakfast. There is no flour left, and the refrigerators have stopped working, but we make do with what we have: a handful of dried nuts and a few flat crackers are almost as good as a fading memory of pancakes. We wait for them to ask where the children are. We watch the way their jaws move as they chew, the bone sliding back and forth under the paleness of skin, and think of how we will answer. They swallow. They take another bite. There is a piece of almond skin between their two front teeth, but we do not tell them. It occurs to us that they are not going to ask where the children have gone.

The existence of our children becomes a secret that we must keep. We close the doors to their rooms. We hide their clothes, their toothbrushes, schoolbooks scrawled across in their hand-writing. Our closets burst with the evidence of their lives. We dedicate ourselves to remembering the moment just before they stepped off of the sharp ledge of ice, how their bare feet kissed the snow as if reluctant to let go, the way their arms swung like pendulums. In our memories, they begin to blend with Isabel Young's son. We give them his first word because we can no longer remember theirs. Some days we remember so clearly how we spoke them out of our mouths the day they were born; other days it seems as though we crafted them by hand from the ice, one smooth curve at a time.

Outside our houses, we recreate them in ice. Our fingers are too thick and too numb to form the sweet curls of their bangs or the dips of their noses—they come out flat, smooth, dull. We hide them too, our ice-children. We keep them at the back of our houses, where our husbands do not go anymore. We make them naked because we cannot remember them clothed, and because in our memories the openness of their skin is so beautiful, so pure. We run fingers across their ice-heels, stretching just a thumb's-length above the ground, barely high enough for us to fit our hands underneath. They are perpetually stretching, the way they are frozen in our minds, the tips of their toes forever on the precipice. We do not give them eyes.

Maybe, we tell ourselves, this is enough. We bring them food that we know they cannot eat, almonds and toast and scabs of dried fruit piled beneath them like offerings. We brush snow off of their shoulders and the curve of their heads. We apologize for the times we loved Isabel Young's son more than them. We realize that maybe we still do, and we apologize again. We realize that we don't know who Isabel Young's son is. We realize that we don't know who our own sons are. We do not know who to apologize to for this. We smooth down the v-bend of their forearms again and again until they are mirrors. We bring our blankets outside.

On the eleventh day of the fourteenth month, we realize we do not want to go inside for breakfast. We spread ourselves out like angels on the snow, and the sky above us is as blue and blank and forever as the ocean on the day they jumped. We imagine jumping. We have dreamed of the ground pulled away from our feet, that drop in the pit of our stomachs like hunger, but we cannot imagine the feeling of the ocean, whether it enveloped them or sucked them in breathless. Our ice-children have no eyes or mouths to tell us. We shake the snow off of our backs and dance our hands over the valleys of their faces. So many steps across and our fingers stop moving and we let them lie there, let their warmth dig channels in the ice-skin of the children we have made ourselves. Our hands stick. We try to pull them away but the ice holds us, or maybe we're just not trying hard enough, and we stand and feel the way the cold seeps into our skin and the sound of the ocean like a heartbeat, crashing angry against our empty islands.

Paper Cranes

MALINA NELSON, Grade 7, Age 13. Gunston Middle School, Arlington, VA. John Stewart, *Educator*. Best-in-Grade Award

Mr. Grier's dog, the half-terrier half-everything else, tears across our yard after a squirrel.

I watch the wiry, spotted fur that blankets his piebald flesh. I watch the thick muscle that convulses as he runs, coating his magnificent skeleton, which cages in his canine heart. I can almost see it, the heart, pumping blood throughout his body and giving him the life that radiates out through his eyes.

I want to dissect him. I haven't told this to anyone, but I need to dissect that dog.

I impulsively make a move toward him, and my hand slams against the window. I bite my tongue to stop myself from shouting in pain.

I flop onto my bed. "It's still alive," I remind myself, shaking a little. "You can't dissect things that are still alive."

I guess Mom must have heard my hand hit the window, because she's standing in the doorway. "You okay?" she asks.

"Yeah." I move to block the window from her sight. Mom hates dogs, and if she sees Mr. Grier's in our yard she'll probably call Mr. Grier, and then he will tell Mom about that one time he saw me pick a dead bird off the sidewalk. Mom knows I like anatomy books. She doesn't know any more than that. I'd like to keep it that way.

"Practicing your origami?" she asks. I turn red, and she smiles. "Okay, well you should. Anyway, if you need me, I'll be ordering dinner in the kitchen. Pizza sound good?" she asks as she saunters out of my room. I don't think Mom has ever cooked anything herself in her life. Artists don't have the time, apparently.

I sit in silence at the edge of my bed for a while, my mind rambling. Only when I hear that obnoxious bark again do I realize that if Mr. Grier's dog catches that squirrel, I might be able to get it from him before he eats it—or whatever dogs do to squirrels. I walk over to my desk and pick up an old shoebox.

I crack open the window and make sure Mom isn't still outside my room before jumping out. Even though our house is only one story, she still gets paranoid that I'll hurt myself.

The dog is still in our yard, and the squirrel is still alive.

I walk over toward the thick patch of English ivy where I built my graveyard. Rocks mark the places where the chopped up frogs and fish and slugs have been buried. And not a single mutilated paper crane.

I turn around and realize that the squirrel has escaped the dog, and now the dog is trotting around with his nose to the ground, evaluating his new surroundings. I groan. I even brought out a shoebox. I stare at the dog. I wonder if he fits into a shoebox.

No. What am I doing? This dog is still alive. And he belongs to Mr. Grier.

I walk over to the fence and peek over. Usually at this time of day, Mr. Grier's out doing yard work, but he must be away somewhere. I look over my shoulder and back at the dog. He seems small enough that I could scoop him up and carry him into Mr. Grier's yard without anyone noticing. I sigh. Anyway, if I just leave him in here I'll probably get accused of stealing him.

I advance toward him and the dog looks up at me. His jaws open and his tongue falls out in a cascading ribbon of flesh and saliva. Dogs have impressive tongues.

As I reach toward him, he darts a few steps away. I try again. He moves again. Realizing that this is getting nowhere, I hold out my hand. In order to examine it, he reaches out his nose. I watch it in all of its scaly, twitching glory. And then the tongue comes back out, this time onto my extended arm, and he drags it across appreciatively.

I move forward and place my hand on his wiry fur. I pick him up. He squirms a bit, but I'm holding him tightly—maybe a little too tightly, but I don't really care. From where my hands are, I feel his heartbeat pounding against them. To prevent myself from tearing him open at that moment, I have to shift them somewhere else.

I walk over toward Mr. Grier's yard. The fence isn't locked, so I push on it with my shoulder. Once we get in, I drop the dog. He runs the perimeter of his yard, and then comes back to me. I try to shoo him away, but he ignores me. His persistence is admirable. Stupid dog.

I dart out of the gate and slam it shut before the dog can follow me. I try and lock it, but Mr. Grier's lock is confusing, so I decide to leave it be. Besides, if he left it unlocked when he went out and then came back to it locked, he'd probably realize that someone had been in his yard. You don't want to mess with Mr. Grier.

I see the pizza delivery man pull in front of our house and I run back to our yard. I pick up the shoebox from where I had left it on the ground, throw open my window, and crawl back inside. I crumple up a few pieces of paper to make it look as though I had been working on making cranes, and then leave my room for dinner.

The evening is uneventful and routine. Mom spends it in her art studio, and I retreat to my room to study the anatomy book until I fall asleep.

I wake up to a bark and then a screech and then a thud. For a minute I lie there, drunk with exhaustion, not quite processing what these three noises might mean. Once I do realize, I get up with a jolt, throw open the window, and practically fall out of it. The night air is freezing. I run through the gate and into my front yard, and then forward onto the sidewalk.

It's dark, but I can still make out the silhouette of a half-terrier half-everything else lying on the road.

Oh my God.

I feel terrible for feeling excited. I look for the car that hit it, but it must have driven away in fear of being arrested or whatever for killing a dog.

I look over at Mr. Grier's house. The gate to his backyard is wide open.

Oh. So maybe I should have locked it after all.

"I'm sorry, Mr. Grier. I'm really sorry, Mr. Grier. Sorry about your dog, Mr. Grier. But will you let me dissect his body? I am very sorry about your dog, but his corpse will serve the charitable purpose of helping me make my anatomical break-through. Please, Mr. Grier? Thank you, Mr. Grier. Sorry, Mr. Grier," I mutter this to myself as I pick the limp body up off of the road. I walk back into my yard and open the window. I shove the dog through, and it lands in an awkward heap on my bed. I crawl in after it.

I switch on the light and glance at the clock. It's 2:00 am. I realize the body is bleeding on my bed, and I quickly transfer it over to my desk.

I sit down in front of it, and grab paper towels off the shelf above me. I then slide open the drawer underneath my desk and take out the anatomy kit. I open the buckles, bask in the glory of its contents for a while, and then remove two jam jars from its depths. I pull out my scalpel and tongs and hold the blade so that it presses against his abdomen. I make a small incision.

I continue to cut through him until the ribcage is exposed. I grab paper towels and mop up the blood that pooled on my desk. I toss them on the floor next to me, too engaged in my work to get up and throw them away. I walk back toward the dog and peer into its gaping body. Even though I have seen it all before—the blood, the bones, the organs—it is incredibly exciting. Maybe because it is on a larger scale this time, or that I've been waiting for this moment since the day Mr. Grier first got his dog, but it is a whole new scale of fascination that I have never experienced before. It is beautiful.

Visit **www.artandwriting.org/galleries** to read this piece in its entirety.

ISABELLE POORE, Brother, Grade 10, Age 15. Paideia School, Atlanta, GA.
Holly White, Educator.

Barrio

ISABELLA NILSSON, Grade 11, Age 16. Hathaway Brown High School, Shaker Heights, OH. Scott Parsons, *Educator*

Ángel de la guarda, dulce compañía

I went to the detention center after school and told him it should never have happened.

He said, "What," and I said dumbass, you dumbass, the baby, and his eyes widened like mine did when I was six and mami slapped me, just to be spiteful, just to make it hurt.

"I didn't know there was a baby," he said, and I said yeah, yeah, well I'm telling you now. "Have you told Mrs. Rodriguez yet?" he asked, and I said do you mean have *we* told mami yet, dumbass, it's your dick, and his eyes widened yet again wider, like it was raining and he had seen a dove skim a puddle, and slipped on a curb.

He was tutoring the kids. Seventh grade, eighth grade, mostly, that dangerous in-between age where you pick between home and parents and candles for the virgin and rice at night, and gangs. The neighborhood, really. Mami and papi want you to be in the neighborhood but not of it, sighing behind shutters and backed up against locked balconies and not flying free in the warehouses and on the storm gutters, because you can get shot that way. It was some university thing, and they didn't pay you any like they did at the bodega, but Carlos said it looked good on the college applications. I told him he didn't have to justify liking it. It wasn't home, and it wasn't the streets, and there were kids who shyly adored you like you were some kind of pro sports player and not a senior in high school with mismatched socks who got girls pregnant—and air conditioning, coldly liquid like lemonade.

"Well, what do we do?" he asked, and folded his hands and I gestured to the little four-foot-tall thing with a lisp and dreadlocks next to him and stamped my foot. You're crazy, I said, Are you for real right now? So we left the fluorescents and the linoleum and the scritter-scratter of monotonous pens and hands trying to fool themselves that they can be something, and we sat on sun-sheathed boxes in the alleyway behind the detention center where I had given him a blow job once because I was high and then prayed for six days. The sky was blue, and people were shouting, and not in the fuck-you-homie-I-gotta-gun kinda way.

I sat on the box. It's *your* dick I said, and started to cry a little, and he said, "Yes, Lola, I know it's my dick, it's not your dick—are you sure?" I'm so late, I said. So I took a test. And I cried more, and it felt like every drop was a bee sting to my eyes, and my heart swelled straight up, and he swore and struck the boxes, which were old banana boxes that he had gripped and moaned, almost feminine, shouting out to the stars, when I gave him that one high blow job in the alley and just before I cried for six days.

"Well, what do we do?" What do you mean, I said. Do you think there's an option? And he blinked, and his eyes fluttered without guile, like a little boy waiting to tug on my dress. Do you want to kill our baby?

"You know I want this with you. But I don't want this with you yet. I can't give it what it deserves, Lola. I can't give you what you deserve. I'm just so young,"

Stop doing that, I said.

"What?"

Acting like that. You can act like you're a little boy because you don't have something sprouting up inside of you, but I won't let you. You're going through it with me, you dick. You and your fucking dick.

"You didn't say no," he said.

Fuck you, I said.

"What do you want to do," he said. "I don't know what to do." Above us a pigeon was drifting in lazy circles black against the blacktop backdrop and falling, falling, gently, like it had wanted to be an eagle and then forgot. I wanted to throw a stick at it, break its wings; bring the pigeon back to earth, where the rest of us had to stay.

Day turned to night like the darkness was tears and God was crying, and I said, O Dios, O Dios Mío, until he had cried the sky black and Carlos said, "I have to go." It was his mom, and she was worried because he had ignored the first phone call, from his no-good hood older brother, and missed calls could only lead to that one big call from the police, that something had happened on the streets, or worse. The morgue. So I said fine, text me, we'll figure it out, comprendas, you dick idiot. And we texted that night and for the next seven days, because we couldn't meet in the detention center or by the wharf or even on our banana boxes in the alley because Carlos got mono and he didn't want the baby catching it.

The first night he told me he loved me, and I said okay.

The second night he told me he loved me, and I said okay.

The third night he told me he loved our baby but only our

future baby and that he wasn't ready, and I didn't say anything at all, just felt the plastic cool from the burn of his text against my chest and stared at nothing and crucifixes.

The fourth night, I slipped out soft at four in the morning so mami wouldn't shout, and I clung to the cold steel of the fire escape and watched the sun rise, orange gushing over the city like the light was a tongue of a wave, lapping up the parks and buildings in tidal intermissions. The cold-faceted steel of the rail pressed up against my ass in my polka-dot pajama pants with the stain on them, and I thought about the sun and being pregnant. My son. My daughter.

The fifth night he told me he loved me, and I said okay.

The sixth night I decided I was getting an abortion.

The seventh night he told me he loved me, and I said okay.

Arroz con huevos in the morning, but I didn't eat because I didn't know if I should, or even if I could. I didn't want to feel the unhatched little chickens slip like sweet rubber down my throat. Mami she said are you okay, is it Carlos again, and I said no. And then I scooted my plastic chair back from my plastic table and I was up, up, through the grille and the front door and out into the sunlight and the sidewalk and the neighborhood in a one-two-three-step swoosh, my Adidas going tap tap tap in the sun and my baby skittering. Even though I knew it was too small to feel it. I'd called my cousin Angelina, la prima mala, always, with the eyebrows tattooed on and the job a hop skip hop above prostitution and an apartment literally above a gun shop and three kids by two different dads and another two she could've had but didn't by a third. That's how I knew she would know. I called her because she knew. And she didn't say "poor baby" and kiss me with her words over the telephone like I needed somebody to, but I could hear the stub of her cigarette going out and the pressing of her lips and

I knew she understood. And she told me get a pen, sí, I know a very good guy, and I got a pen and I wrote it down and I carried the scrap with my baby's death address on it through the neighborhood, and for a minute I thought the secret of it had caught aflame and shone through the wool where it nestled in my sweatshirt. But then I realized it was only the catching of the light.

My phone was there too and it buzzed. Carlos, I thought. Mami, I thought. I didn't want to hear from any of them.

The neighborhood was slipping out from under me like the tongue of a serpent, retracting, retracting. Bodegas and gas places and gun places and Subways and Safeways and the humps of old cars and old men, parked bumper to bumper, idling. The more blocks I walked, the fewer storefronts I recognized, the fewer alleys I had crouched and cried in, and the fewer parking meters my coins had touched. I saw three people I knew on the way to Dr. Zuckerman's office. I saw the abuela of the guy who had saved papi money on his tax returns and then put him in jail gathering up her polyester laundry, and I smiled and I waved because God doesn't like it when you hold a grudge. I saw Paolo the plumber on his off day, feeding pigeons in the park, Paolo who we asked to come over and plumb sometimes even though we couldn't afford it because my uncle had once thrown rocks at him drunk and we were ashamed. And I saw a boy I knew, not well, the kid brother of an eighth-grade ex.

"¿Qué pasa?" he said, and turned his hat around and dropped his pants like I was dumb and didn't know how to get inside them. How's Rico, I said, just to be polite, and because I didn't want to keep going where I had to go with my baby in my stomach.

"Rico's gay now," he said, and spit. "Loco," he said. "But what can you do. More for me. But he's gay. Bet you didn't know that." No, I said.

"You're with Carlos now, right?" He asked like it wasn't a question, and his hat rolled forward over his eyes, which squinted. His tongue kept on peeking wetly out of different corners of his mouth, and I wanted to ask him to put it back in the warm and soft and private place it belonged. Yes, I said. Yes.

"You could do better. You hear I'm riding with the Kings now? Sí, por legit. Riding out this afternoon." The tongue again. "You could do better, mami, is what I'm saying." You're thirteen, I said, I could be your mother. And even though that wasn't true, I felt like it could be, for a second, like he was the baby I kept and so bright and beautiful and riding with the Kings, now, like I couldn't protect him from my own world.

My phone kept on buzzing, again and again. Mami, Carlos, I thought. Like some drum. I walked away as Rico's kid brother threw his head up and cawed like the cock he was.

Zuckerman's office now.

It looked good, like those places where they make your spine crack and say you'll be straighter, or a tattoo parlor that attempted the upscale. Not a doctor's office but up there, close. The woman behind the counter said wait, and I stared at some picture of some revolutionary football in *Sports Illustrated* until I could feel my eyes watering up like floaties in the municipal pool, and stinging like the chlorine. I'd been thinking about God all along, but now I let Him rise up from the bottom of my throat and sit in my head. I wondered if God had been there when I had taken Carlos into my mouth high in the alley behind the detention center and he had wrapped my hair in his hands and moaned, wetly, like a woman. I wondered if He had been there when the drugstore test said Yes, Yes,

You Are. I had felt him like some shawl of certainty all my life, through my communion and confirmation and the hard times, with papi, and the move, with every test I passed and every good thing I prayed for when I lit the candles for Mary, the virgin—but now I hoped He hadn't been watching when I lost my virginity. When the condom broke. So thin, so precious—ultimately useless. I wondered if He were watching me now, what would He say. I felt like a child as I felt my child's imperceivable kicks.

I wished Carlos were there, but he couldn't be there. Again, another buzz. I turned off the phone without looking. The seat was a guilty kind of soft, and all across the felt were little shooting stars.

"Miss Rodriguez? He's ready for you now."

As I walked down the hallway, I thought about God again. I tried to pretend this hallway was taking me to Him and not that other thing, but that stopped working when they put me in the stirrups. A linoleum room. Familiar, almost, like some janitor's closet Carlos would pull me into between kids at the detention center. The doctor said wait, and so I waited, all spread out and spread thin and staring at the blonde in his receding hairline as I watched him go.

I thought about Carlos. We were toddling when we first kissed, five and four and rolling around giggling on street corners trying to catch squirrels. I loved him because he had made it so, kissed me on the lips and laughed like a songbird when I was five and he was four just so that I would never have to wonder what love was, just so I would always know. I loved him because he waited for me with his hands in his pockets in the stairwell of Bugel apartment building, and he had just started to fill out his father's jackets, and when we rode the train to school he would splay his fingers against the small of my back so that they would fit, so that I could never fall. But I hated him because I was seventeen and he was seventeen, and he had done this with his dick. And now I would have to do this, with the scalpel, for him.

When the doctor did it, I felt something go but I thought it was the baby. I can only describe it as a cold, sharp shock, like your body is a string and it is twisted up and held beneath a faucet with the coldest darkest water and then suddenly cut.

"It went real well," said Dr. Zuckerman, when I counted to a thousand and opened my eyes and stepped back into a linoleum barrio world where I was all alone again, but all I could say was God, oh Dios, God, my stomach. I turned on my phone. Carlos could pick me up, now. He could hold me. We would be going to college. He was my punched-up ticket out and the red phoenix on my windowsill. I was seventeen.

But then as they were wheeling me into some other closet, I saw Angelica running (mami came later), Angelica the no-good prima because she knew where I had been, she understood. And suddenly I saw her and the lipstick smeared across her cheeks and I understood, too.

"It's Carlos," she said. "He's been shot." And she answered before I had time to stab my lips through the question. "Muerto, muerto." Who did it, I said.

"He was out looking for you," she said. "He thought you were angry. He called," she said. "I called. They found him in the alley behind the detention center." Not there, I said. Who. My baby. "And guess who did it? Guess who did it?" And she spit and again the things I didn't want to know were answered for me. "Rico's kid brother."

And suddenly I opened my other set of eyes, the eyes inside of me, and stepped out into another place beyond the hallway and the bed, beyond and above the bodegas and jails and parks and rivers and mothers and children and daughters and lovers, into another place where there was no God inside or out of me, and I had killed the Carlos inside and out of me and there was an empty space, a place, a room in my soul with no room in it and only one door, forcing, forcing me back out into Angelica's face and the linoleum place and the barrio.

The funeral was black. I lit the candles, but I didn't really mean it. I tutor at the detention center now. Mami kisses me each day when I go, like a pair of lips on a forehead can glue together broken things. Rico's kid brother is still cawing in the streets, and when I see him I think of the Carlos I could have had and the Carlos I did, and of gunshots and blood in the gutters. Sometimes I get high and cry for six days. I am going to college. My name is Lola Martinez. I am seventeen. Life is ahead of me. It seems so real, sometimes, as I sling my backpack and laugh between classes or eat ice cream and watch sunsets on the fire escape, that it almost seems possible to forget that I had a life, and it died in the barrio.

no le desampares, ni de día, ni de noche . . .

About the Bomb in the Ceiling of the Regent Park Hotel

MICHAEL TROBICH, Grade 12, Age 17. McCallie School, Chattanooga, TN. Erin Tocknell, *Educator*

Strictly speaking, there is a bomb protruding through the ceiling of the Regent Park Hotel. There is insulation hanging off of it in little pink strings of cotton candy, and the bomb itself is painted bright-red and black in garish stripes, the heavy coats of paint obscuring the grayish metal beneath and the hundreds of struts and screws securing the explosive warhead within. This particular bomb dropped from a German plane named "Ich weiß nicht handeln, ich habe gerade machen gesichter," which translates literally to "I don't act, I just make faces." No one working in, staying in, or even generally around the Regent Park Hotel noted this particular fact, not that they would be able to make out the characters painted on the side of the buzzing, diving plane, or that they would be able to pronounce them if they could make them out, nor that they would even be able to translate a correctly pronounced, correctly transcribed version of the plane's name. These would all be out of their capacities, simply because they were English and the plane was German. Because of these two simple facts, a wailing siren blared crimson notes through the abandoned cobblestone streets, and planes buzzed through these misty twilight sirens, dropping hunks of jagged metal that tore through wood and stones and walls with fire and force, and mothers cradled their children in musty basements and prayed for the air raid to be over the way you pray for salvation when you can smell the devil's heavy breath behind you.

If someone had been able to read and translate the name of the German plane that dropped the bomb currently protruding through the ceiling of the Regent Park Hotel, it would have conferred a kind of cruel, triumphant irony onto the bomb itself. This one, unlike the other mountains of metal that fell from the sky in nights of fire and of death, did not explode when it reached its destination. It simply fell, beginning with a moment of no movement when the plane released the creaking doors of the bay and gravity began, slowly, to act on the massivity of steel, and then faster and faster, more eager every second to embrace the welcoming ground, until it encountered the metal and stone and wood of the ceiling of the Regent Park Hotel, which it split like sound does mist. It still sits there now, suspended between the ceiling of the seventh floor and the layers of insulation above, waiting patiently for its purpose to come, for the warhead within it to realize that it has reached the earth and detonate, unleashing fire and force and wind throughout the floors of the hotel, breaking bodies like ragdolls and carrying them through the tastefully decorated hallways, adding stripes of congealing red to the light blue of the walls.

Today is a day after an air raid, and so, there is much bustle and confusion in the streets and hallways, people rushing back and forth, searching for loved ones who they lost in the buzzing and the darkness and the screaming that spread itself between the moments last night. In this hustle, this shifting mass of activity and concern that pulses out among the alleyways and thoroughfares, no one paid much attention to the metal embedded in the ceiling of the Regent Park Hotel, protruding almost comically with cotton-candy strings of insulation tangled in the scattered struts and screws. Lost somewhere in this confusion is a young widow, who lives on the corner of Charlotte and Oxford Street, whose husband joined the army about a year ago, and within a few weeks he was shipped off to an airfield, where he strapped on plastic goggles and a hat whose inside was lined with fur because it got cold flying at twenty-two-thousand feet, and he tended to get nervous when his ears were cold.

Two weeks ago, he was making faces at a German fighter plane's wreckage, which minutes before had been a flying plane with a living pilot, neither of which were true any longer, when he heard a sharp buzzing swooping down behind him. That buzzing behind you when you are in a fighter plane cruising at twenty-two-thousand feet in the air is the sound of death, and he could feel his ears get cold as his hands began to sweat. He banked sharply to the right and left, weaving desperately in the air, but the airplane behind him was a Messerschmitt Bf 109, and the pilot behind its controls did not make faces at burning wreckage sites, he left them behind with cold satisfaction bleeding into the corners of his eyes. He left the young widow's husband in a burning heap of metal and twisted struts and screws, and a week from now she will receive a letter telling her that her husband's plane was shot down far behind enemy lines, and her cheeks will ache from the salty trails of tears. Today, she is casting about in crowded squares, calling out for her son.

Last night, her son was on the roof of the Regent Park Hotel, looking up at the planes. He was somewhere between too young to understand that his father had gone away and old enough to understand that the buzzing and the falling metal caused the twisting tearing fire, so he lay there in the discordant symphony of the evening, among the harsh whistle of steel splitting air, screams echoing down backstreets etched in flagstone, and watched the cruel beauty of the night carve itself into black woolen clouds with black steel shapes diving and falling, tracing the lines between the stars. A few years ago, before the war had started and his father had left, before it was no longer safe to go out onto the roof, his father would carry him on his back as he shimmied up the fire escape of the Regent Park Hotel in quick dark strokes of arms and legs, and they would lay together on the roof, his father pointing out Orion to him in the sky, showing him how he could always find the belt of the mighty hunter by looking for the only three stars that liked each other enough to hold hands. The father had met the son's mother up here fifteen years ago, when the fire escape was first installed, and when they got off of their late-night shifts they found the brushstrokes to paint themselves upwards, to the roof and to the tapestry of violet and orange and fading yellow that was a sunset seen from the top of London. They laid together on the roof and held hands like the stars in Orion's Belt do. The father took his son to where the mother and the father had lain for weeks, searching among the stars for some kind of happiness that they eventually found reflected in the eyes of the other, hoping that maybe he could find some star to call his own and find some kind of happiness in heavy twilights.

Last night, the twilight was less heavy than it was sharp, jagged edges of wings and buzzing tearing through the ever-present fog that gathers in every edge and outline of English buildings. The usual night symphony of voices and steps rebounding off thatched walls was absent, but the night sky was richer than it ever had been before. Planes flew through moonlight, highlighting stripes of bright-red and black and yellow as they dipped and dove and pulled out of their swanlike plunges, leaving gigantic metal eggs to plummet through the darkness and uncoil tongues of orange and yellow flame from the husks of what once might have been a building but now was a painting of fire, force, and twisted metal. The son climbed to the roof of the Regent Park Hotel and watched the planes soar through the sky in a terrible symphony of colors and light and struts and screws, and when he lay back to search the stars for holding hands, he could not find them. He had not noticed the plane, striped bright-red and black like the heap of metal that dropped from its swinging cargo bay doors, swooping down above him, and pulling out of a gently curved descent as its cargo was delivered. He noticed the growing darkness above him becoming larger and larger until it was everything he could see, and then he screamed and now he paints the floor of the seventh floor of the Regent Park Hotel, cotton candy insulation lying around him like scattered flowers.

No one pays attention to the mother casting about for her son in the crowded squares, because to them she is simply another widow trying to find her son in the morning after an air raid, which of course she is, but to her it feels so much more immediate and important than that. She got a letter from the son's father today telling her that all is well at the front and that he needed only one more aerial victory to become an official ace of Her Majesty's Royal Air Force. His letter was written in that looping, loose hand that so many schoolboys develop, the kind that can look beautiful if you tilt your head just a bit to the side and squint just right. Her son was developing the same kind of hand, his p's still loopy, his s's with a particular kind of flourish you could still see traces of in the father's handwriting if you looked closely enough. She wants to show her son the letter, and she wants to remember his father through him, and she does not yet know about the bomb in the ceiling of the Regent Park Hotel. She remembers that hotel as an old haunt of the father, one he'd lurk around and about, chasing shadows into the forgotten nooks of the building, scaling the pocked walls hand over foot, prone on the roof gazing up at the stars every chance he got. She used to watch the stars along with him, but nowadays she reads the papers and is too busy worrying about the war and her son and his father to look up at a metal and buzzing sky.

She is another widow in a city filled with them, a mother without a child, the only difference between her and the legions rereading letters filled with the small parts of the hearts of good men that they could send back in parchment and ink being simply that she does not know yet. In a matter of hours, she will find her son bedecking the halls of the Regent Park Hotel, and she will sink to her knees and question, rightfully, the justice of it all. In a matter of days, she will hear of her husband, twisted and bent and broken among a hunk of flaming wreckage, and the trails of salt striping her face with saline bars will become wider and she will fall to her knees again, alone in her apartment, no longer to protest the unfairness or weep for her lost son and his lost father, but simply to signify her submission, to this heavy sky of war, of buzzing and metal and bombs and garish red-and-black stripes, of rakish orange-yellow tongues stroking the darkness, of stars holding hands and struts and screws containing ripping tearing death. The sky will smile slightly, and another piece of cotton-candy insulation will fall from the bomb in the ceiling of the Regent Park Hotel.

Light-Skinned Luck

ADESUWA AGBONILE, Grade 10, Age 15. The Bear Creek School, Redmond, WA. Kristin Dennison, *Educator*

Oluwadamisi Onajaro had the lightest skin in the whole boarding school. It was the color of a burnt cappuccino, a shade that was so achingly rare it made the older students carry her around with them, like a sort of doll, and call her "Light-Skin Dami." They always clutched her uncomfortably close, as if Dami's fairness was something that would simply rub off onto them.

However, Dami knew that this was not the case: light skin was not something that could be rubbed off. Rather, it was something that had to be rubbed *on*.

And so this is precisely what that light-skinned, Year Ten girl was doing on a pale Tuesday night, feet slipped into soundless stockings, padding stealthily down the dark hallways of her boarding house, clutching her fairness cream with a tight grip in one hand. The night was alive with the chirping of grasshoppers, and Dami stopped and waited for the red-headed lizards to scuttle across the hallway. It was night, and so it was only fair that the true night dwellers had the right of way, instead of illicit dark Yoruba girls who had to rub cream onto their bodies to make themselves light the depths of the night.

It was the time of night when nothing happened, and no one watched. It was the time of the night where you could do anything, and nobody would notice.

Three steps, two steps, one. Dami recited the path she took every night in her head. *Pause in front of the door to Mrs. Onabalo's room* (she was the strictest houseparent in the hostel), *suck in your breath through your nose and tiptoe past her door. Run into the bathroom, close the door behind you, flick the switch, pray there is electricity.*

There is none—is there ever?—and she curses NEPA under her breath.

Luckily, Dami does not need electricity. The day she bought the cream, from an irritable, fat woman backing a snotty baby in the dusty markets of Epe, she brought it home and memorized the places she was going to put it: all over her face, her neck, the upper shoulders, the creases on her arms, her elbows. Thoroughly, so that it would not be obvious that her fair skin was a lie.

It was a routine procedure that, after this night, would never happen again. Of course, Dami did not realize this. She barely even registered the strange stillness of the night, the fact that she could hear her houseparent snoring even though usually the crickets drowned Mrs. Onabalo out. Dami kept on applying cream until she heard the rumble of car tires approaching, muffled only slightly by the dirt road leading up to the boarding house. In the small window up above the mirrors in the bathroom, she could see long shadows drawing nearer, blocking out the feeble light of the moon.

But she did not think anything of it. You see, Dami was a well-behaved student in a good boarding school on the outskirts of Lagos, Nigeria. She greeted her elders, her blazer was always neat, her top button always done, her tie always perfectly creased. She did not have time for imagining the things she had heard about on the news, and she did not bother to think about the whispered horror stories the girls would tell while eating their midnight snack of fresh pineapple. Instead, she continued applying her cream and thought with delight about tomorrow's lunch of jollof rice.

It was only when Dami heard the cars grow even closer that she began to get curious. It was only when she heard them come to a shuddering stop in front of the gates of the boarding house that she started to hear the echoes of best friend Adebola's voice, whispering, *My driver told me they've left the north. They're coming to Lagos. They're smarter than any of us think.* But even then, Dami still managed to twist the cap of her cream jar and dismiss her worries as foolish thinking spurred by the late hour. Then, she heard low sounds. Heavy shoes meeting the ground, things moving around. Her hands were shaking, ever so slightly, still slippery from the cream, and she decided that she would stay in the bathroom just a little bit longer.

A low male grunt managed to travel through the thick humid air, up into the bathroom window, floating gently down to land in Dami's ears. *Da sauri*, the man had said. Hausa for *quickly*. Dami knew this word because all of her Hausa teachers liked to snap it irritably when the students took too long to answer a question in class.

Dami also knew that there were only four teachers who spoke Hausa. All four were female.

On some base, animalistic instinct she retreated, with knife-sharp breaths, into a bathroom stall. Later on, Dami's father would fly her out to London with an extravagant amount of money, hugging her close and whispering *you buy all the fair-*

ness cream that you want, but in that instant, the last thing on the girl's mind was her cream. The latch on the stall squeaked to a close just as—

Bang, crash, boom. Dami knew without seeing that the doors of the boarding house had been broken down. She knelt down on the cold tile floor and finally allowed the two words to enter her mind.

Boko Haram.

You know they kill you instantly, if you're not wearing a Hijab, one girl had said with wide eyes.

They'll kidnap you. Sell you off to the highest bidder. You'll be a slave for the rest of your life, another had murmured darkly, with pursed lips.

Dami was much too scared to cry. Instead, she listened to the footfalls of the men outside the bathroom door. She listened to them walk down the same hallway where she hugged her friends and helped them with difficult homework questions, the same hallway where she had laughed with Adebola about Mrs. Onabalo's triple chin just two hours ago. *Boko Haram,* she thought again, then thought, *No. Never. Impossible, impossible, I am in Lagos. There is no way. No way.*

Yet there she was. Crouched in the boarding house bathroom, cream in one hand, terror in the other. Although many people enjoy using the phrase "cold fingers of dread," that night, Dami learnt that the fingers of dread were hot as hell, humid and stifling, a heat that refused to let you breathe as you sat in a puddle of sweat, motionless, hearing nothing but the blood rushing through your ears and the bloodcurdling shrieks of the girls who were laughing and wishing each other goodnight an hour ago.

An hour ago, or a lifetime ago? Dami could no longer tell the difference.

Harsh words were shouted in deep voices speaking slurred Hausa that was impossible to understand. Even when they switched to English, they spoke in thick accents, and if the men had come an hour earlier, in the calmer guise of fellow teenage girls, they would have been laughed at and called *bush*. Dami could hear the name of Allah being yelled, and she wondered if she was just imagining her friend Aisha—devout Muslim with hijab and all—reciting the Quran. That night, in the bathroom stall, Oluwadamisi prayed to Jesus like she had never prayed before and recited every psalm and hymn that she knew with a vigor that was never present when they had been said in hot assembly rooms with thick itching blazers and no AC.

She did not, could not, *would* not, imagine what she would do if the men came inside the bathroom, opened the stalls, and found her: a chubby, light-skinned, Yoruba Christian girl who still clung onto the faint traces of the British accent she had acquired by spending the first ten years of her life there. She did not, could not, *would* not think about getting up and doing something, calling someone, stopping somebody. It was not until later that she would relive these achingly long ten minutes. It was not until later that these ten minutes would decompose into murky memories that were always paired with saltwater tears that would stream ceaselessly down the cheeks that had faded back to a dark brown. It was not until much too late that she would finally think, *why did you not go out and smash one of the men on the head with your cream jar? Why did you not climb out the window and run to the teachers' hostel and call for help? Why did you sit there like a coward?*

A coward, a little girl, a weakling, a student. Dami would later learn that although these words were used as if they had differing definitions, they all meant the same thing. She learnt this as American and British broadcast stations came trooping through her doors and her father put on the generator twenty-four seven. She learnt this as she dusted off her rusty British accent and recounted the story over and over, and heard the same, stupid phrase over and over: It Was Not Your Fault.

Perhaps it wasn't her fault. After all, she *was* just a little girl, and she had felt like one, sitting in the dark restroom and listening to the muffled cries of her mates. She could hear kicks, grunts, low orders being barked. She could see without seeing: her friends getting tied up, forced into hijabs, hustled onto the backs of trucks, driven off into the murky night to God knows where. She had no way of knowing, but she could imagine with a frightful vividness the pure horror they would have to endure. She could envision Adebola crying in that peculiar way Adebola always cried, with one long hiccup and then a bursting sob. She could imagine Temi swallowing and cracking her knuckles, over and over, until she was sold to the highest bidder and shipped off to whomever, wherever, whenever. Dami could see all of these things, but she did nothing.

She clutched her cream in one hand and took dread's warm, thick fingers with her other, and she did not move a muscle, not even an eyelid, even after she heard doors slamming, engines starting, trucks retreating. Even when she saw the sunlight enter through the cracks in the bathroom stall. Even when her physics teacher opened the bathroom door, saw her feet underneath the stall, and commanded her to release the latch and come out. Dami did not move an inch.

She only stood to her feet and opened the stall door a day later, when she heard her mother's golden honey voice. *Oluwadamisi,* Dami's mother sobbed. Oluwadamisi meant *God has saved me.* And later, during that early time when Dami's mother would not let Dami go farther than five feet from her, she would hold her daughter tight and murmur *God has saved you. Oh, God has saved you.*

Oluwadamisi. It was a beautiful irony, for Dami did not feel saved at all.

Four days after the night of hiding in the bathroom stall, Dami smashed her cream against her bedroom wall and watched it slide down, leaving small flecks of cream and glass splattered on her desk and bookcase. God may have saved her, but only in the most literal of terms. She did not consider the vicious nightmares she got every time she closed her eyes to be a saving. She did not consider the violent fits of tears that greeted her in the morning to be a saving. She did not consider the eerie visits she would receive from the ghosts of her best friends to be a saving. Adebola, Aisha, Temi. Goodbye forever.

Oluwadamisi. God had saved her, but it soon became apparent that he had forgotten about the others. And if God had forgotten, who could be expected to remember?

Requiem

SOPHIE EVANS, Grade 10, Age 15. Lusher Charter School, New Orleans, LA. Brad Richard, *Educator*

In mythology, when heroes died, their forms would be put into the sky as constellations—collections of massive, luminous spheres of plasma held together by their own gravities. If it were up to me, it would be backwards: God would have created the stars and wouldn't have bothered to come up with man. But eventually He needed someone to admire them as much as He did, because God is the ultimate narcissist, and so He made man in his image, and man tore down the canvas that held up the stars without ever knowing that we were created to gaze.

I tell this to my mother as we sit, waiting for our plane, at the Cleveland Municipal Airport. "Are you on drugs?" she asks me, and dabs at her lipstick with a paper napkin. It has come off a little on her Styrofoam coffee cup, a pale red stain.

"Not presently," I say. She's drinking a cup of coffee that cost six dollars, and she asks me if I'm on drugs.

She doesn't laugh. I think that it's certainly convenient that Bill decided to die when school was out. When I asked, my mother told me that my uncle drank himself to death, so I can only conclude that he chose an opportune time to die. When I mention this, my mother corrects me:

"Elizabeth, your Uncle Bill was a manic depressive with a substance abuse problem," which, I think, indicates that I should be sorry for him or for my father for having (had) him as a brother or for my mother for marrying into the family.

"Do you think they're preserving him in alcohol?" I ask, just to be funny.

Horatio Nelson's body was preserved in a cask of rum and brought back to England. When it arrived, however, the cask was opened and found to be empty. Nelson's body, pickled, was removed, and it was discovered that the sailors who'd brought him back had drilled a hole in the bottom of the cask and drunk all the rum.

Missing camp is making me irrationally angry is my thinking on our way off the plane. My mother looks, if possible, more frazzled: Her hair stands on end and her clothes look lumpy, fitting her in the wrong places, at the wrong angles. What she is wearing is entirely inappropriate: a tight orange suede skirt, my father's brown mohair coat and knee-high black leather boots. I don't look much better; my camp T-shirt is grubby, but you couldn't tell under the tie-dye. That's the real point of tie-dye, after all. You can no longer tell what is a purposeful stain or an accidental one. All stains are one stain.

Another thing that makes me angry is families in commercials where the children are genetically impossible because of recessive genes, which is what's playing on the big screens as we stroll down the moving sidewalk. I stand and stare.

"Elizabeth," my mother says, "for God's sake, pick up the pace."

You don't believe in God, I think. Her God is not my God, in any case. Any God that will let her goose-step down the moving sidewalk is not a God of mine.

To Prussia's generals, the goose step said that the discipline and athleticism of their men would withstand all orders, no matter how painful or ludicrous. To Prussian civilians, it said that all insubordination would be ruthlessly crushed. To Prussia's enemies, it said that the Prussian army was not made up just of lads in uniform but regimented supermen. To the world at large, it announced that Prussia was not just strong but also arrogant.

I pull my suitcase up next to her, in front of me, a small barrier. My father will be meeting us soon. I hope he rented a large car but it doesn't matter, because we will be riding to the funeral in a limo with my cousins and my grandmother. This is my first time inside a limo, and I am pretty annoyed that it has to be for a funeral. Ahead of me already, my mother calls back, "Would-you-please-try-to-move-a-little-faster?"

Overhead, the commercial starts up again, and a smiling Aryan family reminds us how much happier they are to be in a studio than this airport. I say, "I want to watch the commercial," because I wonder what fraction of happiness comes from being anywhere but here and if it's significant enough to stop me from making my mother wait while I buy a churro.

"Hurry up!" my mother says, without hearing me. I catch up, catch my breath.

My father meets us outside the airport dressed thusly: a dark sports jacket although it is July, blue jeans, and plastic leather shoes. He is angry because his dead brother, Bill, has an ex-wife who has come to the funeral and is also staying with my grandmother, but there is no time to move to a hotel, so he tells my mother that we will be sharing a house with a family that is simultaneously our own and not. He and my mother do not kiss, and as I expected, the car he rented is not large. I think that this will make the limo more special, more attainable somehow, and less ruined by the overall atmosphere of the event.

Somehow, on the way to my grandmother's house, I don't see anyone a day younger than sixty-five. Even my parents look too old to have successfully fathered me—then I think maybe they unsuccessfully fathered me, which makes me laugh, but not a lot. My mother is trying to catch my father's eye, but he is gone—grieving Bill, maybe, though they weren't close—and so instead she puts on lipstick, red-purple, in the mirror.

In 1770, a British law was proposed to the Parliament that a marriage should be annulled if the woman wore cosmetics before her wedding day.

"How are you, Clark?" my mother finally asks him.

"I'm fine," my father says, which means he didn't eat lunch.

There is not much my mother or I can say to this. "Is Katherine here?" I ask. "And Philip?" These are Bill's children, and though I have never met them, I'm looking forward to it. My father affirms this. Katherine is seventeen and Philip is twenty-one; if Bill intended to kill himself as his second child was leaving high school, he missed the mark by a year, but if he was then he was considerate enough. In technical terms, his pancreas failed, so his death wasn't ruled a suicide, which means he is entitled to a Catholic burial. They found him three days into July by kicking down the door to his apartment.

I remember Bill's voice when I see the program for the funeral, which is on the seat beside me. It reads:

WILLIAM WYATT

DECEMBER 13TH 1966–JULY 1ST 2012

YOU ARE IN OUR HEARTS

And in our pancreases. If I wanted to hear Bill's voice now, I would call my grandmother and wait for the answering machine. His voice is so mechanical that it is almost indistinguishable from the automated voicemail, but I can hear the television going in the background, a news segment on killer bacteria.

After three days, gases in the body tissues form large blisters on the skin, and the whole body begins to bloat and swell. This process is sped up if the victim is in a hot environment or in water. Fluids leak from the mouth, nose, eyes, ears, rectum, and urinary opening.

Did this happen to Bill? I imagine the coffin, sealed shut, full of rum. In science class I held a rat's pancreas and some of it got under my glove so that days later I could still smell formaldehyde like I was being preserved too.

When I enter my grandmother's living room, I think I see five versions of the same person, all dark suits. I'm trying to pick out Philip among these boys, but I can't.

"Hi, Philip," I say, looking at no one, and wave.

"Hey," one of them says, when I thought I had it narrowed down to two. Philip stands up and I hug him awkwardly. Philip is six years older than me, and I cannot help but think that he is kind of tragically cute. Slowly, I take a seat and there is a moment when all of these boys introduce themselves, and I'm thinking, did Philip bring his friends to a funeral? Making a weekend of it. I want to ask him what the last thing he said to Bill was, but it doesn't seem like the right time, because the boys have turned back to the basketball game on the television.

My father made me change into a dress that is also wholly inappropriate for a funeral: linen, puffed sleeves, beige-and-white daisies. In this dress, I feel like I'm going to a wedding. In the kitchen, Laura and my father are talking:

"I need you to sign this," my father says.

"I don't know," Laura says. I met her on the way in—tall, redheaded, prettier than my mother. We hugged, and her body was supple, receiving mine. "I'd feel more comfortable if my lawyer handled it."

"Bill made me the executor of his will," my father says.

"He did?" Laura is surprised.

This is all I hear before Katherine enters in a clopping of heels, putting on an earring. I am jealous. "Hi, Katherine," I say. "I'm really . . ."

"Hi," she says, seeming a little surprised. I wonder what she expected—someone older, prettier? Someone like herself?

"Clark's daughter," I say. I have said this twice already today, a new identity. I wave from the couch.

"I know," she says. Unlike her brother, she has been crying. She addresses him, "When are we leaving?"

"Tomorrow," Philip says.

"I meant for the funeral," says Katherine.

If Philip and Katherine are taking a train from Baltimore to New York City at seventy miles per hour, and Elizabeth is taking a plane to Cleveland at five hundred miles per hour, what is the probability of them ever seeing each other again?

"I'm ready," Philip says. "I can drive us."

"We're going in the limo," I say. "All of us." If we are not riding in the limo, this weekend has been a bust. I want to be pressed between Katherine and Philip like a flower as we tumble over uneven streets. There is something glamorous about funerals.

Q: What's the difference between a limo and a hearse?

A: If you end up above or below ground.

Philip shrugs and his friends shrug too. Laura enters, with my father on her heels, and gives a weak smile. "We're so glad you could make it," she says to me. The next time I see you my grandmother will be dead, I am thinking. Laura perches herself on the edge of the couch, and her hands rub my back. She smells floral, like a funeral arrangement, and her hands are small and heavy. She and my grandmother are making bouquets in the kitchen, petals in everything we eat. The room becomes quiet and still. My grandmother shuffles in, a scarf over her head like an old Russian babushka.

"Oh, Elizabeth," she says, when she sees me. Her face is like a medieval rendering of the Madonna, all pale cheeks and electric eyes and red lips. I stand, part with Laura's hands, and hug her. Her body is wider than mine, doughy like pastry. "I'm just so sad to see my boy go," she says, and I nod, thinking Clark's going and taking me with him.

When she releases me, she pushes back a tuft of white-blonde hair and looks at the room. Laura breaks the silence, "Should we go, then?"

But my grandmother is not ready—if she leaves now, Bill will be dead all over again. She looks out the window, toward the yard. Sometimes there are wild rabbits, but when I tried to take pictures of them, they became fuzzy and dark spots, far-off and unrecognizable.

In the limo I am pressed between Laura and the window, warm on one side and cold on the other. There is a complimentary bottle of water between my knees and I feel inexplicably debonair. No one speaks. I think, *this is paradise. God bid man go out; told him he should no longer occupy and enjoy that garden. This signified the shutting out of him, and all his guilty race, from that communion with God, which was the bliss and glory of paradise.*

At the funeral, I sit in the second pew, between my mother and father and behind my grandmother. Philip and Katherine wave the thuribles; everyone is coated in haze.

Three double swings of the thuribles: the Most Blessed Sacra-

ment, a relic of the Holy Cross and images of the Lord exposed for public veneration, the offerings for the sacrifice of the Mass, the altar cross, the Book of the Gospels, the Paschal Candle, the priest, and the people.

The priest moves around the casket to the altar, blesses us, holds his hands out. The light in here is fragile, like champagne. Dust catches the air, spirals in patterns. My mother sneezes. *Te benedico.* My grandmother shifts her head scarf, flyaway blonde caught in slanting shafts of colored light. Above us, the Madonna glows palely. The casket is still, full, heavy in the air, seems to displace us all.

The priest bows his head, we follow, rows of strangers with their napes facing up. On my knees the stone floor is cool. We are in a closet of the cathedral, a cold and drafty vestibule. Philip and Katherine sit, their clothes heavy with the smell of incense. We raise our heads to sing. My grandmother's voice is throaty, louder than all of ours, rising to the stone ceiling.

My uncle's pickled body. He drank and drank and drank until there was nothing left, not even himself. Thoughtfully, he preserved his insides for us. Another preservation: his voice on my grandmother's answering machine. Katherine's earring catches the light thrown off by the casket, throws it onto my lap, a little warm bead.

V: Requiescat in pace.

R: Amen.

In the back of the limo, my father has left his suit jacket, and in the pocket of the jacket is a letter he wrote to Bill on New Year's Day, two years ago. I read:

"The price of secret is isolation. I'm sure there's truth in the story you have of your life, and how it's come to be that way and why it can't be different. I got uncomfortable with it though, because I thought facts were sticking out through its membrane. Maybe you can construct a better membrane, or change some facts, or hope for friends who don't look so closely."

In another second my mother and father pour into the car and the letter is back in his jacket. We drive on.

At the reception, which is at a seafood-and-Italian restaurant called Rosselli's, I sit at a table with my mother, two of Philip's friends, and my grandmother's sister, Jean. A man in a tuxedo is talking about Bill at the makeshift podium.

"Bill was a hard worker. I don't think he missed a day of work in the eight years he was at Smith and Price." I think this is what killed him. "And Bill was a—he was a real can-do guy. He worked on all sorts of projects with everyone, really—never excluded anyone, really loved—his job, and his kids, and—" The man looks at Laura. "And he was just a really nice guy." I'm beginning to think this man did not know Bill at all. "And I'm sure, if he were here, he wouldn't want to be thought of as—as 'Poor Dead Bill.'"

This makes me smile, and I think Poor Dead Bill. I look at the table to the right of me, where five of my uncle's coworkers exist identically. I think one of you could have noticed this. I think Bill could be alive. I think one of you is dying right now. I think please please please someone notice.

Table of Contents:
Volume 16, Issue 1

ASHLEY GONG, Grade 11, Age 16. Newtown High School, Sandy Hook, CT. Abigail Marks, *Educator*

10 FEATURES / the average American family / according to *Gallup* / one house in the suburbs / a white picket fence / one minivan driven by a soccer mom / 2.5 children / a dog named Fido / but my parents are immigrants / and read me Chinese folk tales / in their native language / while I listened / not knowing about *The Wizard of Oz* / or *The Lion King* / until years later

11 ADVERTISEMENT / insert picture of model here / an hourglass body / sultry gray eyes / ribs that threaten to tumble / out of a sunken chest / insert comment about society / and its impossible standards / but people spend too much time thinking about themselves / to analyze others / so I always go makeup-less / and wear my hair pulled back loose / and tell myself I don't care / but in reality I probably do / I'm just too lazy / to hunt down that missing container of mascara / at 5:30 in the morning

12 POETRY / series of 6 sonnets / quickly scrawled on the bus ride home / while passing by philodendrons / and sprinklers watering dry grass / which stuck out from the dirt like clothespins

15 LITTLE THINGS / the way clothes smell fresh out of the dryer / worn sneakers with faint grass stains / summer nostalgia nipping at the frostbitten ankles of children / the appendix of a little-read book / seven goldfish in an inflatable pool at the fair

16 INTERNATIONAL AFFAIRS / sometimes my grandparents say / that I am becoming too American / in my walk / my talk / my unmistakable air / but over here / people see me as Asian / so I try to stuff two cultures / in one body / but sometimes / there isn't enough room / for both

19 CUISINES / steamed bok choy / udon noodles / always use chopsticks / white rice / moon cakes and grapes / for the October Moon Festival / dumplings for the Spring Festival / but on a Saturday morning / just a leftover plate / of slightly burned pancakes

21 LIFE IN LETTERS / one-word text messages / sleepily typed at 2:00 am / haha / lol / jk / because what else is there to say / in this town / where a fallen tree / or small kitchen fire / makes the front page news

22 NATURE / last week / I boarded the train / and snaked through the veins of the rural land / nothing but low marshes / birds flying south for the winter / not thinking about rigid time / but simply following the whims / of the wind

24 INTERVIEW / daily checklist / are my eyes open / are they really open / is my mind open / how do I feel / why do I feel this way / do I feel energized / am I looking out for my friends / am I looking out for my family / am I looking out for myself / am I in a good place / am I moving forward / am I feeling alright / am I happy

27 PERSPECTIVE / people are dying in faraway countries / or have to walk 6 miles to get water / or go to school / some people / just got divorced / or had an abortion / or just lost someone in a car crash / while I am sitting here / complaining about petty issues / and being the stereotypical / self-absorbed / teenager

29 LANGUAGES / driving with a family friend's mom / who babbles in Chinese / while my tongue awkwardly stumbles / against the shores of Eastern speech / uncooked syllables gritty in my mouth / I can sense her unspoken disappointment /

and my own embarrassment / as her 4-year-old son / speaks with a flawlessly native accent

30 ANAGRAM / confused / dazzled / thrilled / unsure / changing / stagnant / satisfied / ambitious / confident / insecure / fragmented / whole / excited / determined / loving / friendly / self-doubting / nervous / free / independent / alive / proud of my identity / yes, definitely proud

33 ENDING REMARKS / is this where the credits roll / where the curtain closes / when the magazine gets recycled / with the rest of the papers and bottles / but I am far from done / I'm still figuring it out / this changing body / changing surroundings / changing sense of self / this world of chaos / beauty / why my alarm clock sometimes goes off 10 minutes too soon / I don't always know what I'm doing / I don't always know who I am / because this is only the 16th volume / in a life of magazines / all I know / is what I've said so far / all I know / are these sometimes clouded truths / all I know / is that I'll be back / with another issue soon

American Sex Drugs and Rock and Roll in the Age of the Amphetamine Salt

AARON BRONFMAN, Grade 12, Age 17. Deerfield Academy,
Deerfield, MA. Lauren Brozovich, *Educator*

I woke up in the Menagerie of American Cool.
Under the heebie-jeebie shakes and syringes of my junk
withdrawal,
over pages stained with urine and gibberish,
pages, which the night before I had thought to be
honeyed lines of rhythm meter and milk.
I looked to the broken bulbs around the mirror for my
reflection.
A jaundice-eyed scraggled hobgoblin my mother loves to call
Aaron
whose eyelids grate against his retinal agonies
trying to make out the corner where Marilyn Monroe
earns a living fluttering genitals and scarlet.
Scarlet dress blends matching scarlet lips
whose scarlet promises scorched the eyes of presidents.
Behind me I hear Dylan Cash Davis and Howlin' Wolf
warblin' away at the motion of dissidence.
I hear the scritch-scratch of Robert Johnson's pen
as he signs asunder his soul at the crossroads.
The greats make their homes in colorful posters with sickly
paint.
Posters of America,
of American Purpose.

posters of Uncle Sam in his racy
red dress blues,
thumpin' his line at posters overcrowded with flowers
in their dress greens pinks and yellows
Who yak back in beat bubble letters
"FUCK THE WAR."
Then Stanza Break,
Then Silence.
Then Bam! Bam! Bam!
The balled palms of the occupants
bang and bang and bang
against the Plexiglas windows.
The bouquet of the room reeks of the moody blues,
and I can hardly breathe through the cold sweats.
Their dead eyes howl at me but I can't hear them.
My nose is pounding and my head still stinks of smack.
My heart is broken because I know,
I know! I can't help them
I'm too young, ridiculous and late.
It's not all bad though.
I hear the Devil likes the blues,
and sometimes lends Rob Johnson a six string to pick at.
Amen.
I found the relics of Sex Drugs and Rock and Roll in my
father's parlor.
I stupored into it and took the job,
of the zookeeper with no key
At the Menagerie of American Cool.

The narcotic high is coming down.
Outside, rush my generation's most brilliant minds
filled with the contents of textbooks.

They no longer drag themselves through negro streets,
but congregate in the millions for milligrams
Of bubblegum ecstasy.
Pink jumping beans bouncing
to the nocturne of bass speakers
and the acrid hiss of chemical dissolvent
rockin' and rollin' in the frontal lobe.
At least something is.

Rock and Roll is dead.
The notes that moved a nation spent.
We hear melodies of old men frayed from overuse
who our grandparents pay to yell at.
I envy the ear-hair that remembers how the bop bopped fluid,
and didn't try to hip or hop or pop or rap or sell you Pepsi.
They remember the cacophony of stamping feet at the
marches
and the euphony it engendered on stage.
They saw bombs bounce on Iraqi sidewalks
As we clapped away at the four four of the chorus.

The Sexual Revolution is over.
They won.
Commonality in the word "fuck,"
dollars in the word "sex,"
no meaning in "making love."
Passionate freedom is born from monotonous oppression;
but when freedom becomes monotonous, passion becomes
oppressive.
The chase the hunt lust and Internet porn
consume the intellect of our youthful poets and the wallets of
financiers.
Fucking and fucking and fucking each other

In the city evening steaming satin rain.

I take my homework out of my backpack.
Huck Finn's an e-book now,
squished conveniently with
Kerouac Whitman and Ginsberg
in an app next to Angry Birds.
Ms. Donovan's telling me to write about American
Democracy.
About going west and finding open road.
About the courage of the hero and his love of the Dark.
And if we don't abide the wartime tutelage of the academy,
we can't join the legions at Cambridge
or the cohorts in Suburbia,
where the lights are always on and the Dark never got off the
waitlist.
So we cut the lights to drink, smoke, and fuck,
hook eyes to the mouths of bottle-necks
because we can't find a spyglass
and we don't know where else to look.
Drinking and smoking and fucking each other
for this synthesized American Democracy,
the hallucination of an American Dream.

I look away from the Menagerie of American Cool
and join my wayward generation as they stumble past,
For I am too weak to stop them,
And too much a coward to stumble the other way.

Sálganse de la Cocina

GENESIS RIVERA, Grade 12, Age 17. Academy of Our Lady of Good
Counsel, White Plains, NY. Lisa Tallevi, *Educator*

Welcome to Chicanos-r-us
We service all of your needs
Will school principals go to aisle 12?
We still have a few janitors here
Desperate for a job
Yes, they are Mexican
Ready for their graveyard shift
And forget about minimum wage
They are fresh off the border
Give them Taco Bell
They are not expecting any pay
Little girls we just got our new life-sized toys
The hottest couple south of the border
Maria and Jose
They come with a son
A little baby named Juan
And you even get your very own shack
Fully stocked with rice, beans,
Coffee, booze, and burritos
Directors have we the cast for you
The streetwalkers are in aisle 9
Extras that can tango in aisle 10
The big, loud women with hot tempers
They are in aisle 11
But be careful
They do bite
Writing a love story?

We have the most dramatic ones
Sitting in aisle 12
The sexy poor girls that can sing
Are in aisle 13
We even have a special sale on Shakira and Selena
Get 'em while they're young
For you housewives that need 'em
A little more illiterate
And a lot less young
Our Latina maids are in aisle 2
And yes
Their children are optional
Contractors
We have your landscapers
Aisle 6
Prepared to use their brown thumbs
Cheap labor already set to steal
The white man's job
They'll ride up in their pickup trucks
The carpool holds 28
Want it even cheaper
Some don't even need gas money
They come with their own donkeys
Boys lookin' for a bodyguard
You came to the right place
Short and fat with tons of tattoos
They have the guns
That they bought with
The money from their drug cartels
And if you buy in bulk
You can get an entire gang
With 3 members free

Parents we have not forgotten about you
They're breeding like cockroaches
We have thousands of kids
So Brad and Angelina
Please stroll by aisle 5 for pickup
Remember no matter what they say
The information we have given you is correct
Of course, they're all Mexican
There is no such thing
As Ecuadorian, Dominican, or Puerto Rican
They just are uneducated
And have a picture of a police cruiser ready
Just in case they think they deserve a break
For all the Hispanic-Americans in the crowd
You should know that we
Want to keep our company
Not be dragged into a costly lawsuit
So if you were wondering
When we are going to get to you
We aren't
Sí, sí. Hoy por mí, mañana por ti
Pero hoy no es tu día
Y los que no soportan
El calentón sálganse de la cocina
Welcome to Chicanos-r-us
We service all of your needs
And when you run out
Of money for tacos
And dolls,
When 2 dollars
A day is getting
To be too much

We will be there
You will be surprised
By how much we
Learn from
Living amongst you
And caring for your children
And when the day comes
That you address your president
As Mr. Gonzalez
And the Puerto Rican,
Cuban, and Dominican
Flags have been added
To the White House lawn
We will stand up and say,
"Ha-ha Brutos!"
Welcome to Chicanos-r-us
We service all of your needs

2014 Dead Body of Evidence

QIEL THOMPSON, Grade 9, Age 15. Albuquerque ACTSO Educational Outreach, Albuquerque, NM. Jacquelynne Hernandez, *Educator*

Dedicated to E. Garner of New York and T. Rice of Ohio

Hey Black MAN
Hands UP!
Hands out and palms open.
Hands behind your back!
Hands down—
You're guilty

Face off
Face on the ground
Face of a child on a swing
Face it
You're guilty

Walk this way
Walk on the edge
Walk the line
Walk away

Broken neck on a public street
Broken promises
Broken trust
Broken system

Arm of the law
Arms of justice
Arms of just us
Army of one

You're guilty

Black jacks
Black hearts
Black faces
Black robes
Black death

Dead wrong
Dead right
Dead docket
Dead body
Dead dreams

Twenty-first-century life and times
Of the color of law
Colored by the law
Collared by the law

The Difference

DAVID EHMCKE, Grade 11, Age 16. East High School, Sioux City, IA.
Marissa Behan and Wendy Bryce, *Educators*

Staring at the television static, I see such sporadic clusters of
black and white
Even the most basic of things
seems to recognize the difference

I am reminded of black-and-white TV
So primitive
Combining misconception and entertainment illustrated to
little kids
Telling them that this is comedy
Not recognizing that what we were really teaching them was
difference

From then on, we could never really eliminate what was not
the same
All we could see was difference
What was white
What was black
Not what was static
Just what was colored

We'd soon realize that all of our earthly eras are ultimately
painted in different shades of black and white
Color may have evolved, but the ancestry remained
Black and white static roots could not be forgotten

It would take more than Dorothy and Toto's twister for color
to be accepted as mere color

The tornado would need to pick them up and spin them
around in a fury so wild that maybe they could understand

Take them back to Kansas
Take them back to Money, Mississippi
Take them back to Jacksonville and Sanford, Florida
Take them back to Ferguson, Missouri
Where we will hear the screams of black folk so loud
Where a black child begging for help is a reason to put a
bullet in the back of their head
Where the police don't save you, only murder you for your
peaceful surrender

This isn't about me
This isn't about black
This isn't about white
This is about difference

This is about Emmett Till, Jordan Davis, Trayvon Martin,
and Michael Brown
This is about years of necks decorated in nooses, unjustified
murder, strange fruit, and intolerance
Only to be followed by more murder, injustice, and racism

And I'll tell you what,
When they reached the gates of heaven, they were not asked
what color of hood they were wearing
Were not asked how loud they were letting the bass drop
Because God cannot see the difference
Does not know of stereotype
Does not know of racism
Does not know the difference

All he knows is that if Sodom and Gomorrah were leveled by
brimstone, why is Ferguson still standing?
Why is Mississippi still standing!?
Why are we still standing on the sidelines, watching our
nation's children be slaughtered under a regime that sees
color as motive!?

I have been waiting for a colorblind nation to prevail out of
ash for too long!
Our vision must be restored
Or else we bleed out
We drown
We hang from trees like strange fruit swinging in the breeze

And this isn't poetry
This is unfiltered rage
One can only stare at static for so long before he too becomes
colorblind
Reduced to nothing but black and white

So I'm singing this song for you, Emmett Till
I'm singing this song for you, Jordan Davis
I'm singing this song for you, Trayvon Martin
I'm singing this song for you, Michael Brown
Because if I don't sing
I must conform
And if I conform
I will only see the difference

The Will

JULIANA CHANG, Grade 12, Age 17. Taipei American School,
Taipei City, Taiwan. Kaity Kao, *Educator*

Give my dresses to my daughter.
Let her know she was never made to wear my shadow,
but these dances are hers to keep
if she wants them.
Send my skinned knees back to the tree
where I first learned how to climb,
my tongue to the snowflakes that could never land quite right.
My feet go to the beach where I first fell in love.
Please keep all calluses as they are.
As for my spine, tell them to build a staircase; any staircase,
it's carried me for so long
I want someone else to have a try.

When you untie the love that once kept me one,
remember not to cry. An unraveling is not an ending.
Direct my atoms to the trees, wave as they go.
The time will come
when you bump into them again

(and the day you start to laugh like before,
return my keys to the corner behind the sofa;
they always liked sitting there)

Lucky

KALI FILLHART, Grade 11, Age 17. Appomattox Regional Governor's School, Petersburg, VA. Cindy Cunningham, *Educator*

I don't remember unemployment
rising, or families going hungry.
What I remember is
not getting that neon green, high-speed
mountain bike I wanted for my tenth birthday,
not going to the movies on weekends anymore,
eating more TV dinners and microwavable cuisines.

There was never a figure thrown around,
never anything mentioned about
the economy. I don't remember
the transformation of money becoming
less of a useful inanimate object, like a lamp or sofa,
and more like the medication my mother took
to calm her nerves. A necessity.

I never saw any of it. Only the
tension between my parents tighten,
their late arguments growing
deeper into the night, the headlights
of my mother pulling out of the drive,
into the midnight, full-moon-lit world
that transformed the homeless and hungry
into stargazing romantics like herself.
We were lucky and it hurt.
We were lucky and had no right to complain
about our empty cabinets and broken car windows.

Mr. Superior

DE'JOHN HARDGES, Grade 10, Age 15. Cleveland School of the Arts High School, Cleveland, OH. Danny Gray, *Educator*

I saw dis drunk
On deh corner of 1-0-5
Wearen' deh same thang
Dem red-and-white Jordan's
Wit deh black check on deh side
But, I sweah he told me
Dat he stood in line deh first time
Wen dey first came out
Den tell me why he rocken' deh Dickies real baggy
A black ROC-A-
WEARen' it proud
Dat was his armor
Made him bulletproof
Wit all deh rips and holes
Even wit his fitted cap
You could definitely tell dis character from a caricature
Breath reeking hottah than deh devil peeing whiskey
Constantly staren' n' preachen'
On that same corner
Smellen' of the same thang
People say the same thang
Story changed but same thang everyday
He claims he's seen it all
But his eyes, solid gray
Everybody say he's lost it but, I think he hella sane
I listen
Facts is all I hear

A primary source, sound like he was right there
Everything becomes vivid
Deh stench of each picture
Speak descriptions only he could hear
Now he pass 'em on to who eva he catch listenen'

One time
One time
He told me 'bout a conversation
He had wit dat house on the corner
Like 3 different colors
Dey had a discussion
Dey criticized bein' loyal
To compromises
Becuz' nuthen harder den self-reliance
Out here on these mean streets
Dats how he said it
He had a sense of humor but that's not why I didn't forget him
He was actually wise
So I respect 'em
Aim a few dollas his way
Jus to get 'em rejected
He would tell me
Deh superior sign told him not to accept it
He claimed my ear was enough
So I continued to lend it
As he told me where he found
That shell of a building
It was deh late '80s
He said
A few cops and a gang
Were bumpen' heads

A couple dozen shots
Left everybody dead
It was horrible
Building jus had to be condemned
But it still caused trouble
You know suicides
Or car accidents
Boom!!! Into deh brick entrance
Deh city got sick of it
So dey tried to tear it down
But it kept resisten' 'em
Left a shell there
And a few skeletons
Talked to 'em all
Before he cleaned up
Den settled in
Claimed it
After dey mangled it
Deh city's trash
Became his settlement
Living life
Is wat he claim he does
Every day on dat corner
Getting extremely drunk
But wen I ask, his response
Is I'm jus a lil buzzed
I don't think he crazy
That's jus sumn you labeled 'em

Ears listenen'
To broken records
Broke ears

from passing that paper
I'm done hearen' yo

Aye—Look at this
A no-named pic in the obit
Says he had no family or a place to stay
No one knew his identity
He nevah wore a mask
Said he was a drunk
That's jus how y'all pictured 'em

But really he was superior

What If?

CHASITY HALE, Grade 10, Age 16. Miami Arts Charter School, Miami, FL. Jen Karetnick, *Educator*

"What if the raindrops get so big,
they swallow the sky?" she asks.
Could we use the papers
in the glove compartment
to start a fire and illuminate
the liquidated skies?

We'll use every rusted coin
to purchase blessings,
and buy plane tickets to destiny,
where we will find a milk carton child
and wish her home to voices
tainted with "We'll find her" and
"It gets worse before it gets better."
We'll get our names in the newspaper.

What if we're happiest when we are sleeping?
I'll fold your skin like origami
until you are a swan or a flower
and I will place you in my pocket
so that you can nestle in the warmth
like a baby bird.

My daughter tries to climb her way to heaven
by shimmying up stalk-like tree trunks.
We live in a godless place, but treat it
as if there is plenty of god left in you.

I tell her to roll the windows down.
To love not the smell of rain,
but the smell of it leaving.
"What if the clouds taste like Peppermint Patties
on the train that travels over the ocean?"
"What if it is heading to nowhere in particular?"
"What if that is where we want to go?"

Bird-Throated

AIDAN FORSTER, Grade 9, Age 15. Fine Arts Center, Greenville, SC.
Sarah Blackman, *Educator*

1.
The sky ringed with flames and children's tears,
palms bent in the wind like Aztec women washing their hair,
a chemical imbalance of metal and flesh.

Peering through the arrow slit of your shield
you might see the god Huitzilopochtli—
only the worthiest of you will see each of his feathers,

undulating shades of summer, a brazen sunset,
and stare into his dilated pupils. All of you
will become hummingbirds upon death.

2.
Do I have to wait for death
to turn me into a hummingbird?
I'm peering through the leaves at the sky—

it's golden, as if Midas had fallen from the stars
and touched every cloud on his way down.
The streets pitch with light,

my dog sniffs furiously. She's golden, too—
naturally tawny and tinged with this alien afternoon
she looks Egyptian in her regality.

Tomorrow someone will say
she thought the sky was falling, it was so foreign.
The sky couldn't fall, though—

the dog around the corner would have to stop barking.

3.
Somewhere along the way
we all turn into hummingbirds.
It's inevitable, a coup d'état

to rival that of Napoleon. Death
holds ruby feathers between his skeletal fingers.
God is bird-throated.
Children's tears can fly backwards and forwards.
Fingers groping in the dark and the barrel
of a gun are both slender beaks

that drink from beating hearts,
nectar from a hyacinth.
All the arms in the world are just

silver cages. Maybe in the womb
we were hummingbirds, floating in that milky
light and sipping from placentas

with our fragile beaks. In the rope of life
the knots will fray, and the curtain of our existence
will fall to something greater, a kind of Armageddon

not found in department store windows. In that inky
blackness,
confronted with the absence of ourselves,
surely we'll mimic the sunset, shed our skin

like thinning clouds and burst with colors.
Life and the passage of time is just a kind of waiting
for gemstone aviation and eggs the size of pennies.

monster

MAYA GILMORE, Grade 12, Age 17. Sheridan High School, Sheridan, WY. Matthew Johnson, *Educator*

they call you monster, laughing,
      ignoring how
your face crumples,
adam's apple bobbing
         convulsively.

     (it's the costume
blood red lips, shadowed eyes
          black dress.
   it's the way
        you chose
   to be yourself.)

you pretend
     you didn't mean it
and it's okay
when they cross the street
     and warn their children of the 'monster'
because it's all one big joke.

all a joke
     the way your skin
     crawls, an infestation of insects
straining to squirm away from your skeleton
       the way-too-big bones and overdeveloped muscles
     slither round your heart, a constrictor
suffocating any scrap of self-esteem

the way each pronoun
stings like a spider bite,
poison seeping into your blood coursing toxic—

but it's okay.
of course, it's okay.
it's just a joke, and you
were only ever just
a monster

Hunted

JIYOUNG JEONG, Grade 11, Age 16. Milton Academy, Milton, MA.
Lisa Baker, *Educator*

At a shark market in Fujian Province, China
bruised neon signs roast
the moon, fresh blood bubbling
on fins packed in Styrofoam.

The shark's eyes
look like black
marbles she used to play with
and she hates to watch
his corpse soak up gore as
rice paper would drink octopus ink. She
remembers her calligraphy class—*Too much ink
will tear the paper.* Beside her he lies
like a strip of shadow, as

She had on the battlefield—
fingers woven across her M1952A Flak
vested chest, short breaths spitting
automated prayer, every rib rising to
build a grave
a grave for laughter, a grave for kisses, for
murmured dreams. *Someday
I would like to swim again,* the shark whispers, and how
she yearns to set him free, reassemble
his tongue and gullet, carcass torn to feed human
nonsense—*God, let me
see tomorrow.*

Cities.

EILEEN HUANG, Grade 9, Age 15. High Technology High School, Lincroft, NJ. Sarah Gross, *Educator*

"Every city has a sex and an age which have nothing to do
with demography. Rome is feminine. So is Odessa. London
is a teenager, an urchin, and in this hasn't changed since the
time of Dickens. Paris, I believe, is a man in his twenties in
love with an older woman." —John Berger

phoenix
is disheveled brown hair and
too much eyeliner and
hard gray eyes,
half-asleep on the fire escape,
one hand tracing the papery outline of his cigarette,
the other dangling off the edge precariously, toward the
sirens,
all in awe at his quiet nonchalance.
he blows two trails of smoke,
lost in soft grayness.
his eyelids flicker
and the city wakes with him.

new orleans
dances
with supernovae in her hair,
swallowing note by colorful note
from the mouths of the trumpet players,
wrapping the music around her,
like a warm bath towel
after a swim in the mississippi.

she sings the words when she doesn't know them
but she doesn't look up,
doesn't care,
doesn't need to.

indianapolis
writes love letters to chicago and new york
but never sends them.
she hides them under her bed
tucked away in a yellow box
under her yellow comforter
she takes two out and reads her own looped,
tangled handwriting.
one for new york,
one for chicago.
(sealed with a kiss)
she reads until she's cross-eyed and
her eyes feel like sandpaper,
puts them back in the box
and shuts the lid.

juneau
goes to the movies by herself on sunday afternoons
to watch scorsese films
at the only theater in town, near the fishery and the dentist's
office,
stuffed between the jeweler and the shoe shop.
the film starts,
the screen glows.
she taps vaseline onto her dry lips
drinks a coffee, black—
hands cold as yukon snow, always—
and starts reading a copy of a movable feast that she'll never
finish

san francisco
lives in a one-room apartment
hanging above the bay like a bird cage, dangling,
overlooking the rough shadow of alcatraz.
at noon he goes to the wharf
and talks to strangers about novels and classical music and
silicon valley
he laughs and it sounds like waves crashing against ferries,
like french fries hitting the grill, saltwater bristling against
hair.
but at nights he goes out,
to listen to the lone guitar player,
and hears each lonely string
echoing through the dimlit bar.

Ode to Welles

EMILY MACK, Grade 11, Age 17. Northside College Preparatory High School, Chicago, IL. Dianne Malueg, *Educator*

City parks like campuses, canvases
where make-out-session lessons get buried
under shallow wood chips and bruised legs search
for home in streets that will never love them back,
we paint sky lines with swing-set bars and rust bubbles.
The Ancient Romans used to give wedding bands
engraved with the words: *I don't love you enough*
and those words might feel like rejection under
modern fingertips like lines on a slide when you go down
too fast, modern thighs, I always go down too fast, the word
slut gets thrown like sand, but this park is just a classroom,
we came
here with pens and bandages for the learning experience,
field training.

The local teen bands circulate, circular like wedding bands,
engraved—I think what the Romans meant was I don't love you
as much as you deserve because no one ever could
and it's romantic but all I have is lines on a slide, janitor closet
memories—Lily said teenagers will make out with anything
because we're all so lonely and I can't say I disagree as we lie
here beneath the bouncy metal bridge, its squeaks
menacing beneath light-up gym shoes—who knew
we'd end up down here together or out there, moving
in rhythm along tennis court dance floors but still too cool
for homecoming.

We could hide here so long we forget to seek,
lose freeze tag and remain eternally still under
the trees, we could wait for years here, palms outstretched
until we get so old that new batches of parents call the police.
Roman women were made for marriage and for breeding
and on the eve of their wedding, they left their childhood
dolls on the temple altar. If they died before that,
the toys got buried with them—get buried under
shallow wood chips and gazebo goddess light.
City park, I don't love you enough.

The Peach Pit

JOE POLSKY, Grade 11, Age 17. The Fieldston School High School, Bronx, NY. Rebecca Wallace-Segall, *Educator*

Monday
On Monday her foot scrawls dizzy arcs on the carpet.
The elevator swells with pride
and lifts us up into orbit.

Tuesday
On Tuesday we read the newspaper
and dream of papier-mâché.

Wednesday
On Wednesday our lazy planets brush
we lean our legs against the wall
I wrap my hands in her shirt and
the arches of our feet shatter.
Her heels touch ground
with a sound like china
when it is empty and struck.

Thursday
There is a space in my chest where
a peach pit grows in the mothy dark.
It is a very small space, damp and rough.
On Thursday, she grazes it with her palms.

Friday
On Friday she knits our hands together
and shows me her constellations:
Ursa Major of the six freckles on her lower back,
Andromeda and starlight spilled across her neck.

I was blue today, she says.
But that's all right now.
I touch my hands to her waist, God
my nerves . . . they twitch and they bud.

Saturday
We pass Saturday drowsy on the carpet
I brush the shipwreck of her ribcage
with the backs of my hands.
There are a thousand candles in her stomach
for this moment, they have all been lit.

Sunday
We eat breakfast with the dawn still sticky above.
There are a thousand gestures we could make
to keep the rain lofty.
Instead we make conversation over soft toast.

The rain is coming, but we are naked
underneath all our wrappings.
I walk in socks because there are lakes
groaning beneath the floorboards.
They ache to be fed.
I'm feeling blue again, she says.

Nighttime is growing
in the flowerbeds that litter the cul-de-sac.
We watch it from our windows
then put on our shoes.
Forgive me, for
the rain is here.

Snapchat Summer

MAIA ROSENFELD, Grade 12, Age 18. Winchester Thurston School,
Pittsburgh, PA. Judith Sanders, *Educator.* Creativity & Citizenship Award

I press my thumb to the screen,
hold down the half-eaten pie next to your name
and watch as you giggle-shriek
with shirtless boys and almost-shirtless girls clutching red
Solo cups and carelessness.
Your flat-ironed hair falls into the frame, hides faces
you probably won't remember when the time runs out
and these moments are deleted, forgotten
like they never happened.

Your summer hides in an app on your phone, and a million
views won't make it real
enough, your picture frame memories will never be as real
as folk songs and sundresses,
late night whispers about him and then and what-if.
Yours is a pictures-or-it-didn't-happen kind of summer,
an is-that-even-candid type of summer, a temporary, public,
only-'til-you-lift-your-thumb Snapchat summer.

Your summer is pixilated and fleeting.
When your phone runs out of memory,
will you, too?

Sometimes I wonder if sunsets existed before Instagram.
Maybe they just weren't as pretty
without a filter, without followers, without seventy-two likes
to tell them they were beautiful.

Paper Dolls

AUDREY SPENSLEY, Grade 11, Age 16. Avon Lake High School, Avon Lake, OH. Stacey Hallett, *Educator*

> That's the best thing
> a girl can be in this world,
> a beautiful little fool.
> —Daisy Buchanan, *The Great Gatsby*

I.
My mother taught me
how to hold myself
like a swan's neck. Elegance
hides in the sloping curve.
Elegance always hides. I said
I had chipped myself away
like a nail—
the manicured surface
unspooled, ragged.

III.
Take your blade, core me
into summer fruit—rotten
and soft. You can't run
with ankles knotted in silk.
You must practice fluency
in a language of fluted crystal,
pearls shackling your wrists.
You can't hold on to fleeting
birds. Best to just snip
the wings.

IV.

I press myself between the pages
of a photo album, and I build
a home there. Once I dreamt
of starting fires with a single touch,
crumbling empires with the flick
of a finger. You must learn
to ignore the cold grate of regret
curdled in your stomach.
Don't touch the matches, darling,
unless you're sure you want to burn.

JEFFREY WAN, *Cacophony*, Grade 11, Age 17. Novi High School, Novi, MI. Jennifer Harvey, *Educator*.

Letter to My Boy-Man

RACHEL CALNEK-SUGIN, Grade 12, Age 18. Hunter College High
School, New York, NY. Dan Kitrosser, *Educator*

I don't know whether to call this boy-man
a boy or a man
because a man means he should know better
and a boy means his mother should take the blame.

I wish I were a chameleon
I mean the fruit-roll-up tongue
unraveling to catch a fly
like throwing the scroll of a holy book
down the stairs,
I mean I wish I could make my skin
the same color as
walking home from a party on Riverside
after curfew.

I don't want to call this boy-man
anything except the boy-man
who threw me against a wall and made out with me;

I bet he is a nice boy-man who loves his sister
I bet he is not thinking about her
and has had two drinks too many
I understand what it is like

that you feel it has been forever
since you were last thrown
against a wall, and I bet
you miss my lips until

I'm trying to push you
off with them—
did you know the tongue
is the strongest muscle in the body
relative to its size? I'm dwelling
on tongues, I know,
because I can't seem to get yours
out of my mouth,
and I have bruises to prove it
grayish purple all up
my arms, I told my mother
I fell off my bike
since I knew I would be punished
for being thrown against a wall, boy-man.
I'd never be allowed out at night again,
to sit on a fire escape
with somebody I have loved
for a long time,
watching the stars and feeling like
the world was a very good place.

When you pin me there
in your strong muscles,
pushed up hard against me
I go limp against your mouth
like undoing drawstring pants.

I don't want to fight
with anybody, boy-man.

Walking away is harder
than writing a poem about walking away,

and I have imagined this scene
so many times, the stranger
on Riverside, after curfew,
that I am no longer scared of it.

Boy-man:
am I supposed to fight you off now?
I am not a lion.
I am 17-year-old girl,
self-righteous and bossy

and feeling obligated to mention
my halter-top
even though there is nothing inherently erotic
about shoulders,

except sometimes, boy-man,
I see my boyfriend's shoulders
all silhouetted in the moonlight window

and I want him to grab me
and throw me against a wall
and leave bruises,

he touches now, a gentle
forefinger on my
forearm, asking where they came from.
I cannot bear to tell him
about you, boy-man,

the way you will not go home
to tell your sister about me.

Broadripple Is Burning

GRETA WILENSKY, Grade 11, Age 16. Lowell High School, Lowell, MA.
Maribeth O'Neil, *Educator.* Best-in-Grade Award

The third-story bathroom is full of women. They lounge on
the linoleum,
their bodies tired as ripe fruit. Listless. Maria lights the joint
and passes it around,
an olive branch, a common thread. Jenna gnaws on the inside
of her cheek.
Her teeth have eroded into tiny mountains. They remind her
of where she's from.
Appalachia, trailer-park youth, a mother with a mouth black
as night inside.
Methamphetamine, she knows now. Eleanor has knitting
needles and wears her hair
in a thin braid that reaches the small of her back. She stays
quiet, like always.
Some say she's in love with a woman, older, a pilot who died
in a freak accident,
a red-eye plane crash into Japanese forest. You don't want to
ask her, though,
because if you do she'll lower her glasses and do that thing
with her eyes,
that scathing glance. Victoria was a burn victim. Is a burn
victim, she says,
but with money like hers comes doctors with chrome waiting
rooms and glittering scalpels.
The surgery went so well they used her in the brochure. She
is glossy pages

good to look at. Amina is the only one who won't take a hit from the joint as it's passed around.

She has a head full of braids and bracelets running up her arms.

Her laugh makes you unfold. Hot sand on the beach. Gifts from a foreign country.

The men are nowhere to be seen—this is a given. A silence understood.

The men are boys and they have restless hands and twitching knees.

Their women are always listless, and so they leave them rotting like fruit.

Peach pit. Lengthwise center of a grapefruit. Strawberry, apricot.

An oyster but without the salt, without the wincing.

The women know this and are getting sick.

The pattern of the bathroom floor tiles is etching itself into their thighs.

How to Steal a Storm

EMILY ZHANG, Grade 11, Age 16. Richard Montgomery High School,
Gaithersbug, MD. Todd Stillman, *Educator*

Saturday the rain forms a film, the air cold and sweet,
a backwards mausoleum, the cars outside blinking like teeth.
My sister learns about reincarnation
by writing a letter to god. The first line: here's to owing
the world who I was at sixteen. My sister with kohl
loped around her eyes, curling her lashes with the backs
of safety pins, taking lessons in shoplifting. How last year,
she was caught meditating in the back of a burning car,
pushing against a boy like a tidal wave, vultures in her throat
spouting lines about metaphors as apologies. A ritual
in reverse. The second: six years ago a man on the telephone
told her to put her hands between her thighs and squeeze
and she told him nothing, except about her doppelganger who
lives in hell, who was born in a man's earlobe and went
on a date with you, a boy, a god in place of a god.
That was back when the universe was first beginning,
when they both saw a bird drop its friend in a trashcan.
They never kissed. The third: please, if she were
to be reincarnated, keep her as a baby. She says nothing
more, but I see her, shifting in a current of static. A compass,
a wave, north. My sister was supposed to get an abortion
but she didn't and now I'm an unreliable narrator. I'm sorry.
I lick the salt of the envelope lip closed for her. She forgets
to address the letter.

Ringing Bells: A Sonnet

ADAM WACKS, Grade 8, Age 13. Millburn Middle School, Millburn, NJ.
Judith Lindbergh, *Educator*

When once I wandered to and fro the night
I pondered every drip of word for years
Lost myself in lacking any fears
Slammed the door of morning at first light.
You fought me for your glittered plastic crown
But I climbed until I played the mortal game
Claimed the ringing bells for my own name
In morning flames your whisper could not drown.

Today I stride far beneath the light
And when these bitter hours come around
Although I burned your vision to the ground
Your gaze never wavered in its right:
But I will keep the promises I've bound
Impossible to bend, and so I fight.

Why Do Buddhist Monks Wear Orange?

HENRY HEIDGER, Grade 12, Age 17. De Smet Jesuit High School, St. Louis, MO. Robert Hutchison, *Educator*

Why is the sky blue?
The question of youth is why

do people die? It was a question
of uncertain results

until biology class explained
everything. Herded us to believe

in lines, single file from room
to room like sheep. In my textbook

I saw a photograph. In France
the children cross their arms

in the monastic style.
Folded across the next page: why

do Buddhist monks wear orange robes?
We figured the figure showed

orange is in abundance
in northeast Thailand. A textbook

example: they had orange. We had blue
popsicle stains around our lips

and kissed the thought
of monks in meditation.

Then I saw the lush, green ink
and realized they had more colors than

my father's palette of oils.
Now chemical dyes

are used and sometimes give
that vivid orange color

that one sees in Bangkok.
But why do clouds move faster

when they're eggplant gray
and filled with a jar of rain?

Is it because the sky's fertile
rows of soil are sown

by airplanes zipping up the seams?
Or is it because I asked why,

and the sky was too nervous to answer?
She zipped up her cleavage,

turned her cheek away from me.
She cried a saffron sunset

over the jungles of Thailand,
and turned the soil orange.

Beautiful monks grew
like tiger lilies.

Poetry Recitation at a Girls' School in Parwan Province, Afghanistan

ALETHEIA WANG, Grade 11, Age 17. Homeschool, Verdun, QC, Canada.
Una Wang, *Educator*

Before the worn blackboard, girls
take turns standing at attention, facing

the teacher with clasped hands,
their faces peeping from their hijabs, their eyes

softly aglow with certainty, filling the silence like
falling snow. They hold their heads high and recite poems

they have carried in their mouths for days.
I long to be as young and wistful as they, to feel words

rising in me like bees heavy with pollen. The girls
sing each verse, swaying like the slender trees

whose branches, dusted with gold, shade the schoolhouse.
I want to sing with these girls who will grow

into or away from their bodies.
Each girl trembles with honey-warm language

blossoming full in her mouth,
lost in the blaze of the poem that holds her.

When the girls finish reciting, their eyes widen
in wonder, as if they have folded up the ocean

within them. It's how all great dramas end:
everything is restored but safety.

Ocean Song

TOPAZ WINTERS, Grade 9, Age 15. Singapore American School, Singapore. Doug Behse, *Educator*

I've learned that life is a funny thing. it works
in mysterious ways: ships sink slowly, water
rises quickly. everyone is an artist nowadays:
fill in the lines, color in the blank spaces. blue
paint runs down the page. sea foam blurs
careful brushstrokes. I'm no masterpiece, but
I've learned how to hold a pen, and I've learned that
maybe that's enough for now.

I've learned that *for now* is an important phrase,
that tomorrow I will grow into someone brand new.
I've learned to be okay with that. the universe
does not care whether I'm happy, but sometimes I
listen to the ocean singing in the shoreline's ear:
youarelovedyouarelovedyouareloved, on and on until the
end of forever, and I hear the words to the ocean's
song and think perhaps the universe is leading by example.

I've learned that I am so much more than the
numbers that try to define me. I've learned that
words are the most important weapons I can hold,
and I'm learning how to wield them with care.
oceans and brushstrokes don't make a poet,
but they do make a person, and I've learned that
maybe that's enough for now.

I've learned that sometimes the ending isn't a happy one,
but I've also learned that sometimes it is. I've learned that

backbones are more valuable than wishbones. I've learned
how to say yes to myself. I've learned that my body is a
shrine and if no one else worships it, then I must be
my own goddess.

I've learned that life works in mysterious ways, that ships
are sinking around me and it's not easy to stay afloat. I've
learned that perhaps the ocean isn't singing only to the
shoreline. I've learned that words can be anchors or
deadweights, and I'm learning to tell the difference.
I've learned that there is no end to the battles I can lose.
and I'm learning that I am worth every one of them.

NATHANIEL ATKINSON, *Renewal*, Grade 11, Age 16.
Harrisville Junior / Senior High School, Harrisville, NY.
Jade Atkinson, *Educator*.

ABOUT THE AUTHORS

NAMAN AGARWAL likes to write absurd essays for English class by suggesting that every author is imitating Karl Marx. He enjoys writing about topics like philosophy and psychology. He based his memoir off of other stories, which, if you think about it, doesn't really make sense.

ADESUWA AGBONILE is a Nigerian-American living in Seattle with an affinity for long books, loud music, and Netflix. She's always had countless stories floating around in her head. After years of trial and error, she's discovered that the best place to put her stories is on paper.

RON ANAHAW has a long history of bad nicknames and lame punchlines. Words that come to mind to describe Ron are "mischievous," "Libra," and "eats-all-the-cashews." He uses writing to trick people into one-sided conversations where all they can do is nod and turn the page. He writes on the bridge between humor and melancholy.

JULIA BELYUNG lives in Brattleboro, Vermont. She loves her guinea pigs, dubstep, playing the cornet, ice cream, swordplay, and Pathfinders. She can often be found spending drowsy afternoons with her nose in a book.

ALISON BOEHMER is an avocado. Like the vegetable, she is thin-skinned—she melts at the mention of mistreated books, women, or shoes. Her "green, meaty" layer is composed of dedication to herbal tea, running trails, and correcting strangers' grammar. At her core resides her true passions: falling more in love with her King, conscious capitalism, and words.

AARON BRONFMAN was raised in New York City and attended high school in Deerfield, Massachusetts. He is a husk puppeteered by a dangerous cocktail of stimulants and impulse. He writes poetry and music to express the struggle to stay in his own good graces.

RACHEL CALNEK-SUGIN writes so that she can figure out what she actually thinks. She is happiest with an avocado, a cup of coffee, and a good book. Rachel will be a freshman at Yale University this fall.

JULIANA CHANG read her first poem at the age of six, and the world hasn't stopped spinning since. She has big dreams of being a poet-neuroscientist. When she isn't writing fictional wedding toasts and obituaries, Juliana enjoys eating any and all forms of potato, playing with her dog Momo, and learning Latin.

OLIVIA DABICH lives just outside of Washington, D.C. She enjoys running, discussing free speech with her dad, eating anything from Trader Joe's, and playing Apples to Apples with friends.

JO DE WAAL lives in America during the school year, but over the summer she lives in the Netherlands, in a village surrounded by a moat. As she is half Dutch, Jo is curious about cross-cultural exchanges. Riding her bike across polders is Jo's cure for writer's block.

TRACE DEPASS's writing addresses inequality and the faulty justice that arises from it. He believes that it is the duty of artists to expound upon the issues of their time. Trace will be attending Brooklyn College in the fall.

DAVID EHMCKE hails from Sioux City, Iowa, where he can be found sloppily eating a doughnut or reading *The Washington Post*. Often, he writes about social issues in the United States and politics of the body. A firm believer that "words make worlds," he hopes his writing will inspire others to create worlds of their own.

SOPHIE EVANS was born, probably, and started writing sometime after that. Her writing is her tell-all, where she balances her own awkward sense of self with the commotion that surrounds her. She lives in New Orleans, Louisiana, with her three poodles (Delilah, Balzac, and Théo).

LIZZIE FIERRO spends most of her time crying over poetry, learning new languages, and eating as much Tex-Mex as humanly possible. An aspiring activist and diplomat, she hopes to explore topics of social justice and human rights in her work.

KALI FILLHART will one day be important enough to be worth knowing, but at the moment she is simply another teenager trying to make it in the world. She likes bagels and cream cheese, reading, exercising, and chilling with her nine-person family. She owns a snake and more journals than she can fill.

AIDAN FORSTER is often found reading overpriced poetry books and eating Reese's Peanut Butter Cups. A champion overuser of adjectives, he is interested in exploring his sexuality in poetry and often writes about the ocean, birds, church, and boys. He is an avid fan of Mark Doty and gemstone necklaces.

JACK FOSSETT is a screenwriter and student at the School for Creative and Performing Arts in Cincinnati, Ohio, where he has been taught to be a socially conscious citizen of the world. His work often revolves around travel and features young and/ or queer protagonists.

When not writing, CATHERINE GAO loves to dance, listen to music, bother the neighbors with her singing, and take long showers (although not anymore, because sometimes the rain gods forget about California). She draws inspiration from the people around her and occasionally takes public transportation simply to watch the people who walk in and out at each station.

MARELLA GAYLA is an incoming Harvard freshman from New York City with a love for Vice President Joe Biden and a flagrant potty mouth that she probably shouldn't display in this bio. She writes to challenge existing narratives, whether they are literary or social.

Though monstrous when her reading is disturbed, **MAYA GILMORE** is usually cheerful, philosophic, and absent-minded. She was born and raised in a small town in the Big Horn Mountains of Wyoming. Her interests include dance, calculus, linguistics, art, anthropology, LGBTQ concerns, and most importantly: poetry!

SOPHIE GLESSNER has been writing stories since the fourth grade but hasn't truly believed her words held meaning until last year or so. She is inspired by celestial bodies and the wonders of coffee. She works to maintain a level of "real" in her writing.

ASHLEY GONG hails from Connecticut. For her, writing is a medium through which she can answer—but more importantly, ask—questions about the world around her. Most of her best ideas come late at night or while riding various forms of public transportation.

CHASITY HALE has been writing ever since she discovered the gravity of words. Her hobbies include biking, running, and cooking. She also has great interest in social activism and popular culture. Chasity has a true fondness for all fine arts, but her love of poetry extends possibly even further than Kanye West's love for himself.

DE'JOHN HARDGES is a student at Cleveland School of the Arts pursuing a career in literary arts. He writes every day. He recently discovered a passion for performing original pieces and has performed at several venues in Cleveland, including the

Kennedy Theater at Playhouse Square and the Rock and Roll Hall of Fame.

JORDAN HARPER is > you, is bae, and has a blood type of Bey-positive. His writing includes, but is not limited to, laughable executions, sea lion love affairs, reality television families, and Siamese twins. He is currently working on escaping the Confederacy.

EDIL HASSAN's lyrical work conveys both nostalgia and longing. While contemplating trauma and the aftermath of exile and diaspora, the warmth of her poems and short stories will stay with you long after the last word.

HENRY HEIDGER is a writer and poet currently residing in the Midwest. He loves typical things such as nature, traveling, and sunsets. However, he also loves things such as urban exploration, strong espresso, and Gregorian chant.

Alleged anarchist and confirmed voracious reader and writer JENNIFER HORSBURGH is known for ranting about politics. She regularly dispenses unsolicited opinions, facts, punk-rock song recommendations, and invitations to wake up and change a piece of the world.

Currently a student at a STEM school in New Jersey, EILEEN HUANG enjoys reading anything from cereal boxes to Kurt Vonnegut. When she's not typing biology objectives or doodling on her engineering binder, she writes poetry and paints still lifes. She believes that there is still a place for words and language in a silicon world.

Although she rarely gets out of bed early enough, JIYOUNG JEONG absolutely loves the morning stillness that motivates her to write at 5:00 am. She habitually carries around a notebook and a pen so that she is prepared when the inspiration for a new poem pops into her head.

KIMAYA LECAMWASAM has been trying to discover the meaning of life for nearly seventeen years. But after a move from Massachusetts to Arizona, ten years of martial arts, a gig as a singer-songwriter, and a series of clumsy falls down the stairs, she's learned that it's ok to be confused. It gives her something to write about.

Hailing from a small town in Maine where the number of churches exceeds the number of traffic lights, LIZZY LEMIEUX uses both poetry and fiction to explore her Jewish identity and place in the outside world. She loves to travel but will always come back to Maine for the coastline and summertime.

Self-titled "America's Number One Fan," MAYA LEW loves a good laugh, a good read, and her great country. This young patriot is an avid reader, writer, pun-maker, and reality-TV-watcher.

EMILY MACK is a Chicago kid, born and raised. She attends Northside College Prep and does most of her writing while sitting on curbs waiting for the bus.

NOAH MAINS dislikes conventional wisdom, improper use of statistics, and unnecessary teen angst. Due to his unerringly wholesome and tragedy-free early life, he's forced to find topics for his works among a sizable stack of newspapers and nonfiction reading. He strives to set a morbidly optimistic middle ground in his writing.

GRANT MCCLURE is from Charleston, South Carolina. He plans to concentrate in Environmental Studies at Wofford College next year. When he's not reading or writing, he can be found tying flies at the local fly shop or wading the flats in search of tailing redfish.

Many have asked MALINA NELSON how someone could possibly be so unintentionally macabre. It begins innocently enough: She wants to tell the stories of characters she finds interesting. Unfortunately, most people end up perceiving them as psychopaths.

"ALEXANDER NGUYEN's funny but he's kinda awkward. He seems asexual, but I think he's gay. Yeah, he's smart, but he tries too hard. Why are his lips so big?" He listens and pretends he doesn't hear. He won't speak up and try to change the way the world feels about him. He thinks he'll write to change the world instead.

ISABELLA NILSSON is half Swedish, half Puerto-Rican, and bad at any sort of math that doesn't involve basic fractions. She reads David Foster Wallace non-ironically, but will occasionally indulge her inner hipster by donning a black turtleneck and listening to records on reclaimed vinyl.

ARRYN OWENS is a dedicated athlete, musician, writer, and student, as well as a native Seattleite with a passion for the outdoors. She has never really considered herself a writer, but rather a middlewoman between words and reality. She is inspired by the wonders of the world she lives in and the people and experiences that have shaped her.

RACHEL PAGE learned at an early age that she can't sing, dance, or act, so she turned to writing as a last resort to make her voice heard. She writes because she loves words and because she's forgotten how to do anything else.

ALEXIS PAYNE believes that art retains an unparalleled power as an important function of all revolutions, rebellions, and forces of social change. As a writer, words are her method of choice to express the things that anger and inspire her the most. She loves playwriting and poetry, and she will be attending Yale University in the fall.

Bedtimes meant nothing to six-year-old JOE POLSKY, who stocked his bedroom in New York with flashlights to support a reading addiction that has only grown stronger with age. He writes poetry because he's the kind of person who would argue with the wind, and in a poem you can build your own weather patterns.

JAE HAENG RHEE spends most of his waking hours painting, philosophizing, drinking both high- and low-quality coffee, writing fiction, and wondering why he does all the aforementioned things. He finds the world's existence thoroughly astonishing and tries to capture its weirdness and beauty through his creations.

Though raised in Miami, Florida, HANNAH RICHTER has many homes. Some are physical, like Palmetto Senior High School and Washington University in St. Louis (come 2016). But perhaps her most important homes are not so easily defined—the spaces between sentences, the valleys in the Blue Ridge Parkway, the cartridge inside a pen. However, ars est ubique.

GENESIS RIVERA is a half-and-half blend of Puerto Rican and Dominican blood, which must be the source of the intense passion she feels in her pursuit for universal justice. She was raised in an inner-city neighborhood, but moving to a quiet suburb opened her up to the insights and discrimination on both ends of the spectrum.

MAIA ROSENFELD is from Pittsburgh, Pennsylvania. She has been writing since before she could tie her shoes and has become proficient in both the "loop-de-loop" and "bunny ears" methods. Maia writes everything from plays to poetry, peppering her works with scenes from her life and overheard conversations.

AMELIA ROSKIN-FRAZEE is an openly lesbian teen from San Francisco who loves writing untold stories and telling bad jokes. When not doing either of those things, she can be found working on her organization (The Make It Safe Project), playing badminton badly, and contemplating how strange it feels to write about herself in the third person.

AUDREY SPENSLEY lives in Avon Lake, Ohio, where she attempts to read David Foster Wallace novels and take her cat for walks, both of which do not usually end successfully. Through her writing, she seeks to explore how concepts like identity, family, and feminism are being redefined in today's technology-soaked world.

When she's not editing her school's newspaper or staying up too late reading, **ABIGAIL SWOBODA** is still editing and staying up too late—but instead, she's telling the story. Whether it be fiction, nonfiction, or a combination of the two, she always has a story on her fingertips.

When she's not preoccupied by her iPhone or listening to music at maximum volume, **MONIQUE TAYLOR** can most often be found with a pen in hand, writing on every available surface—often including herself. Her dream is to one day bring poetry back to the center of the public eye as an art form.

QIEL THOMPSON had the unique experience of growing up as part of a blended family. He enjoys the systematic approach of math and science, but loves the escape of writing and visual art. He wants to pursue astrophysics and is determined to find a way to blend science and art.

JACK TIEN-DANA is from New York City. He can often be found yelling at his television during Knicks games. Raised by two writers, Jack writes because it is the only life he has ever known.

MICHAEL TROBICH is an incoming freshman at Kenyon College who loves David Foster Wallace, Haruki Murakami, and whitewater kayaking. If you're taking his order, he'd like an apple cinnamon scone and a cup of strong black tea, thanks.

CAROLINE TSAI is the editor-in-chief of *Mimesis*, her school literary magazine. She is the recipient of the 2015 Canterbury Book Prize. This summer, she plans to attend the Kenyon Review Young Writers' Workshop and the Iowa Young Writers' Studio. Caroline enjoys NPR, traveling, and Jane Austen.

KINGSLEY-WYNN UKUKU is a sixteen-year-old Nigerian-American who spends far too much time on her phone. She enjoys reading about people who enjoy reading, falling in love, solving mysteries, and long walks on the beach. She cares greatly about the Oxford comma.

AMELIA VAN DONSEL is semi-agoraphobic and enjoys mockumentaries, new stationery, and setting the microwave for odd amounts of time. Writing brings her a sort of solace and rush that nothing else can. She hopes to pursue writing professionally alongside her love of physics.

ADAM WACKS is a poet and drummer who is constantly at odds with himself. When he is not busy biking in circles around suburban New Jersey, he enjoys playing card games with strange names and features. He writes because he notices his surroundings and because he needs to bleed out the ink lodged beneath his fingertips.

ALETHEIA WANG has traveled to twenty-five countries and lived in six of them. She believes in stories and in laughter. She is especially thankful for her mother, who taught her to read and love books. If she were to write an autobiography, she would title it *I Thought It Was Inspiration, But It Was Just Caffeine.*

A happy teenager in sunny California, CHRIS WANG is an enthusiast of food, golf, travel, and reality shows. He also has a knack for critical thinking. He hopes to inspire others to reflect and act upon social issues through his creative writing.

GRETA WILENSKY is a high school student from Lowell, Massachusetts. Her writing focuses on queerness and the intricacies of growing up. She spends her time ringing up people's groceries, buying too many lattes, and rambling on about Drake's evocative capabilities to strangers.

TOPAZ WINTERS is sometimes a rapscallion, other times a shattered epiphany of almosts, and most of the time both. She writes thank-you notes to the universe and love letters to the people who have made their homes there. Slightly incorrigible. Excessively weepy. Vaguely poetic. And so forth.

EMILY ZHANG is from the boring suburbs of Maryland. Outside of writing, she volunteers at a farm and teaches science at a local elementary school. She likes watching reality television, and she considers the Whole Foods cheese section her second home. She prefers nouns over adjectives.

CONGRATULATIONS TO THE
EDUCATORS BEHIND *THE BEST TEEN WRITING OF 2015*

Angela Ackerman
BASIS Scottsdale
Scottsdale, AZ

Jeanette Amiano
Waltham Senior High School
Waltham, MA

Lisa Baker
Milton Academy
Milton, MA

Marissa Behan
East High School
Sioux City, IA

Doug Behse
Singapore American School
Singapore

Sarah Blackman
Fine Arts Center
Greenville, SC

Wendy Braun
School for Creative and
Performing Arts
Cincinnati, OH

Colene Brockman
William Fremd High School
Palatine, IL

Lauren Brozovich
Deerfield Academy
Deerfield, MA

Wendy Bryce
East High School
Sioux City, IA

Donald Carlson
Trinity Valley School
Fort Worth, TX

Wes Carter
Kennard-Dale High School
Fawn Grove, PA

Mara Cregan
Pittsburgh CAPA 6–12,
A Creative and Performing
Arts Magnet
Pittsburgh, PA

Beth Cronin
Newton North High School
Newtonville, MA

Kathy Crutcher
Woodrow Wilson Senior
High School
Washington, D.C.

Cindy Cunningham
Appomattox Regional
Governor's School
Petersburg, VA

Kristin Dennison
The Bear Creek School
Redmond, WA

Martha Erskine
Marymount School
of New York
New York, NY

Stuart Flynn
Alabama School of Fine Arts
Birmingham, AL

Nick Geary
Goose Creek High School
Goose Creek, SC

Katherine Geers
Mission San Jose High School
Fremont, CA

Marci Glessner
Sheyenne High School
West Fargo, ND

Scott Gould
South Carolina Governor's
School for the Arts
and Humanities
Greenville, SC

Danny Gray
Cleveland School of the
Arts High School
Cleveland, OH

Royce Gregory Jr.
Klein Forest High School
Houston, TX

Sarah Gross
High Technology
High School
Lincroft, NJ

Lyndsay Haag
BASIS Scottsdale
Scottsdale, AZ

Stacey Hallett
Avon Lake High School
Avon Lake, OH

Kerry Herlihy
Gorham High School
Gorham, ME

Jacquelynne Hernandez
Albuquerque ACTSO
Educational Outreach
Albuquerque, NM

Robert Hutchison
De Smet Jesuit High School
St. Louis, MO

Lucas Jacob
Trinity Valley School
Fort Worth, TX

Matthew Johnson
Sheridan High School
Sheridan, WY

Lori Joynes
Nixa High School
Nixa, MO

Kaity Kao
Taipei American School
Taipei City, Taiwan

Jen Karetnick
Miami Arts Charter School
Miami, FL

Susan Katz
Riverdale Country School
Bronx, NY

Dan Kitrosser
Hunter College High School
New York, NY

Patrick Lagmay
Thomas A. Edison Career
and Technical High School
Jamaica, NY

Mary Lenning
School for Creative and
Performing Arts
Cincinnati, OH

Judith Lindbergh
Millburn Middle School
Millburn, NJ

Dianne Malueg
Northside College
Preparatory High School
Chicago, IL

Abigail Marks
Newtown High School
Sandy Hook, CT

John McRae
Canterbury School
Fort Wayne, IN

Jason Meyers
Miami Palmetto Senior
High School
Miami, FL

Mamie Morgan
South Carolina Governor's
School for the Arts and
Humanities
Greenville, SC

Susie Mortensen
Lakeside Middle School
Seattle, WA

Flor Mota
McCallum High School
Austin, TX

Martha Noone
Marshall High School
Falls Church, VA

Maribeth O'Neil
Lowell High School
Lowell, MA

Scott Parsons
Hathaway Brown High School
Shaker Heights, OH

Brad Richard
Lusher Charter School
New Orleans, LA

Rebekah Rogers
Saginaw Arts and
Sciences Academy
Saginaw, MI

Caroline Rosenstone
ACES Educational Center
for the Arts
New Haven, CT

Judith Sanders
Winchester Thurston School
Pittsburgh, PA

Jeff Schwartz
Greenwich Academy
Greenwich, CT

Seth Slater
Carroll High School
Fort Wayne, IN

Lucinda Stein
Gorham High School
Gorham, ME

John Stewart
Gunston Middle School
Arlington, VA

Todd Stillman
Richard Montgomery
High School
Gaithersbug, MD

Joyce Sullivan
Brattleboro Area
Middle School
Brattleboro, VT

Suzanne Supplee
George Washington Carver
Center for Arts
and Technology
Towson, MD

Lisa Tallevi
Academy of Our Lady of
Good Counsel
White Plains, NY

Erin Tocknell
McCallie School
Chattanooga, TN

Jennifer Touchton
Leland High School
San Jose, CA

Eve Tyrrell-Berinati
Burlington Senior High School
Burlington, VT

Robin Von Breton
Lick-Wilmerding High School
San Francisco, CA

Rebecca Wallace-Segall
The Fieldston School
High School
Bronx, NY

Una Wang
Homeschool
Verdun, QC, Canada

AN EDUCATOR'S GUIDE TO *THE BEST TEEN WRITING OF 2015*

Use the works of these award-winning teen writers to inspire discussion and guide writing exercises with students.

1. Short Story—Discussion on characterization and voice—35 minutes

Goal: Students explain how authors establish the voice of a narrator to create distinct characters who inform a reader of time, place, and mood.

Activity: Introduce the concept of a story's "voice" by having students discuss popular first-person narratives as well as close third-person narratives that are particularly different and compelling.

Next, choose a piece with highly engaging character voice(s). As you're reading out loud, have students mark any points in the text where we notice specific character establishment through the tone of the prose, dialects, slang, humor, or other details. After you're finished, have students discuss the following:

• What does the author want us to know, or understand, about the narrator of this story?
• How does the separation of character voices establish a reliable—or unreliable—narrator?

In partners or groups, have students select a narrator and describe his or her personality. Then have them return to the text and find specific details (speech, thought, and interaction with others) to illustrate the narrator's personality and how it informs and shapes the narrative. Share student responses.

2. Short Story—Writing with focus on characterizing the narrative—35 minutes

Goal: Students restructure a narrative with another narrator, creating the same story with a different perspective.
Activity: Ask students to take on the voice of one of the other characters and tell the story from that point of view, filling in blanks that the original narrator did not. Challenge students to use important characterizing details in the reading to give color to their entries.

3. Poetry—Writing with focus on form—30 minutes

Goal: Students write using different structural techniques.
Activity: Have students write two poems on one topic of their choosing. Begin with a prose poem, in which they write freely on that topic; then have them write another poem on the same topic with a focus on line breaks to emphasize changes in rhythm or highlight specific phrases. Discuss the differences after sharing the results.

4. Personal Essay/Memoir—Writing with a focus on structure and pacing—45 minutes

Goal: Students will write an organized and coherent memoir imitating the format of a *Best Teen Writing* piece.
Activity: Select a personal essay/memoir from the anthology to read out loud with your students. Talk about the format in which the memoir is written. Discuss the choices made and how those choices are inherently personal, therefore inherently suited to convey a personal essay.

Ask your students to write their own memoir modeled after the memoir you have selected. Have the students share their work and discuss choices that each student makes, including how those choices convey something personal to the reader.

5. Genre-Shifting Exercise—40 minutes

Goal: Students will explore form's relationship to function by converting a piece in the anthology to another genre. For example, reimagine a play as a poem; a personal essay/memoir as a science fiction/fantasy piece.

Activity: Have the students choose a favorite piece in *The Best Teen Writing*, then have them reinterpret that work in another genre. Afterward, have the students compare the original to the genre-shifted piece and discuss how the same information is relayed through contrasting forms.

6. Blog Exercise—40 minutes and homework time

Goal: Students will use critical-thinking skills to offer critiques and analysis of specific works or the anthology as a whole.

Activity: Ask students to write a blog post expressing thoughts about a specific piece of their choosing. Posts will be sent to the Alliance for consideration to be included on the Alliance blog.

• Students should express their opinions, offering positive feedback or constructive criticism, on a specific work in *The Best Teen Writing*. Alternatively, they may discuss the anthology as a whole.

• Posts may be e-mailed to **info@artandwriting.org**, with subject line "The Best Teen Writing of 2015 Student Blog Post."

Educators: Continue the discussion! Explore with your peers even more ways in which *The Best Teen Writing of 2015* can inspire students in your classroom! Visit the Vision and Voice website, presented by the National Writing Project, at **www.visionandvoice.nwp.org** to learn more.

REGIONAL AFFILIATE ORGANIZATIONS

The Alliance would like to thank the regional affiliates listed for coordinating the 2015 Scholastic Art & Writing Awards.

Northeast

Connecticut
Connecticut Art Region
Affiliate: Connecticut Art Education Association

Delaware
Delaware Art Region
Affiliate: Delaware State University

Delaware Writing Region
Affiliate: National League of American Pen Women,
   Diamond State Branch

District of Columbia
DC Metro Writing Region
Affiliate: Writopia Lab

Maine
Maine Art Region
Affiliate: Maine College of Art

Southern Maine Writing Region
Affiliate: Southern Maine Writing Project

Massachusetts
Massachusetts Art & Writing Region
Affiliate: The School of the Museum of Fine Art
   and *The Boston Globe*

New Hampshire
New Hampshire Art Region
Affiliate: The New Hampshire Art Educators' Association

New Hampshire Writing Region
Affiliate: Plymouth Writing Project

New Jersey
Northeast New Jersey Art Region
Affiliate: Montclair Art Museum

New York
Central New York Art Region
Affiliate: CNY Art Council, Inc.

Hudson Valley Art Region
Affiliate: Hudson Valley Art Awards

Hudson-to-Housatonic Writing Region
Affiliate: Writopia Lab Westchester & Fairfield

New York City Art & Writing Region
Affiliate: Alliance for Young Artists & Writers

Twin Tiers Art Region
Affiliate: Arnot Art Museum (serving parts
   of New York and Pennsylvania)

Pennsylvania
Berks, Carbon, Lehigh, and Northampton Art Region
Affiliate: East Central PA Scholastic Art Awards

Lancaster County Art Region
Affiliate: Lancaster Museum of Art

Lancaster County Writing Region
Affiliate: Lancaster Public Library

Northeastern Pennsylvania Art Region
Affiliate: Marywood University

Philadelphia Art Region
Affiliate: Philadelphia Arts in Education Partnership at
the University of the Arts

Philadelphia Writing Region
Affiliate: Philadelphia Writing Project

Pittsburgh Art Region
Affiliate: La Roche College & North Allegheny School District

Pittsburgh Writing Region
Affiliate: Western PA Writing Project

South Central Pennsylvania Art & Writing Region
Affiliate: Commonwealth Connections Academy

Southwestern Pennsylvania Art & Writing Region
Affiliate: California University of Pennsylvania

Rhode Island
Rhode Island Art Region
Affiliate: Rhode Island Art Education Association

Vermont
Vermont Art & Writing Region
Affiliate: Brattleboro Museum & Art Center

Southeast

Florida
Broward Art Region
Affiliate: Young at Art Museum

Hillsborough Art & Writing Region
Hillsborough County Public Schools

Miami-Dade Art Region
Affiliate: Miami-Dade County Public Schools

Miami-Dade Writing Region
Affiliate: Miami Writes

Northeast Florida Art Region
Affiliate: Duval Art Teachers' Association

Palm Beach Art Region
Affiliate: Educational Gallery Group (Eg2)

Pinellas Art Region
Affiliate: Pinellas County Schools

Sarasota Art Region
Affiliate: Sarasota County Schools

Georgia
Georgia Art & Writing Region
Affiliate: Savannah College of Art and Design (SCAD)

Kentucky
Northern Kentucky Writing Region
Affiliate: Northern Kentucky Writing Region

South Central Kentucky Art Region
Affiliate: Southern Kentucky Performing Arts Center

Louisville Metropolitan Area Art Region
Affiliate: Jefferson County Public Schools

Mississippi
Mississippi Art Region
Affiliate: Mississippi Museum of Art

Mississippi Writing Region
Affiliate: The Eudora Welty Foundation

North Carolina
Eastern/Central North Carolina Art Region
Affiliate: Barton College

Mid-Carolina Art & Writing Region
Affiliate: Charlotte-Mecklenburg Schools

Western North Carolina Art Region
Affiliate: Asheville Art Museum

Tennessee
Middle Tennessee Art Region
Affiliate: Cheekwood Botanical Garden & Museum of Art

Mid-South Art Region
Affiliate: Memphis Brooks Museum of Art

Virginia
Arlington County Art Region
Affiliate: Arlington Public Schools

Fairfax County Art Region
Affiliate: Fairfax County Public Schools
Southwest Virginia Art Region
Affiliate: The Fine Arts Center for the New River Valley

West

Alaska
Alaska Art & Writing Region
Affiliate: Young Emerging Artists, Inc.

Colorado
Colorado Art Region
Affiliate: Colorado Art Education Association

Hawaii
Hawaii Art Region
Affiliate: Hawaii State Department of Education

Idaho
Idaho Writing Region
Affiliate: Boise State Writing Project

Nevada
Northern Nevada Art Region
Affiliate: The Nevada Museum of Art

Northern Nevada Writing Region
Affiliate: Sierra Arts Foundation

Southern Nevada Art & Writing Region
Affiliate: Springs Preserve

Oregon
Oregon Art Region—Central Oregon Area
Affiliate: The Oregon Art Education Association

Oregon Art Region—Portland Metro Area
Affiliate: The Oregon Art Education Association

Oregon Art Region—Willamette Valley Art Region
Affiliate: Benton County Historical Society

Washington
Washington State Art & Writing Region
Affiliate: Cornish College of the Arts

Snohomish County Art Region
Affiliate: Schack Art Center

Midwest

Illinois
Chicago Writing Region
Affiliate: Chicago Area Writing Project

Mid-Central Illinois Art Region
Affiliate: The Regional Scholastic Art Awards Council of
Mid-Central Illinois

Suburban Chicago Art Region
Affiliate: Downers Grove North and South High Schools

Southern Illinois Art Region
Affiliate: John R. and Eleanor R. Mitchell Foundation /
Cedarhurst Center for the Arts

Indiana
Central/Southern Indiana Art Region
Affiliate: Clowes Memorial Hall of Butler University

Central/Southern Indiana Writing Region
Affiliate: Clowes Memorial Hall of Butler University and
Hoosier Writing Project at IUPUI

Northeast Indiana and Northwest Ohio Art & Writing Region
Affiliate: Fort Wayne Museum of Art

Northwest Indiana and Lower Southwest Michigan Art Region
Affiliate: South Bend Museum of Art

Iowa
Iowa Art & Writing Region
Affiliate: The Connie Belin & Jacqueline N. Blank International
Center for Gifted Education and Talent Development,
University of Iowa

Kansas
Eastern Kansas Art Region
Affiliate: The Wichita Center for the Arts

Western Kansas Art Region
Affiliate: The Western Kansas Scholastic Art Awards

Michigan
Michigan Thumb Art Region
Affiliate: College for Creative Studies

Southeastern Michigan Art Region
Affiliate: College for Creative Studies

West Central Michigan Art Region
Affiliate: Kendall College of Art and Design of
Ferris State University

Minnesota
Minnesota Art Region
Affiliate: Art Educators of Minnesota

Missouri
Missouri Writing Region
Affiliate: Greater Kansas City Writing Project

Nebraska
Nebraska Art Region
Affiliate: Omaha Public Schools Art Department

North Dakota
North Dakota Art Region
Affiliate: Plains Art Museum

North Dakota Writing Region
Affiliate: Red River Valley Writing Project at
North Dakota State University

Ohio
Central Ohio Art Region
Affiliate: Columbus College of Art & Design

Cuyahoga County Art & Writing Region
Affiliate: The Cleveland Institute of Art

Lorain County Art Region
Affiliate: Lorain County Regional Scholastic Arts Committee

Miami Valley Art Region
Affiliate: TEJAS Gallery/K12

Northeast Central Ohio Art Region
Affiliate: Kent State University, Stark Campus

Northeastern Ohio Art Region
Affiliate: Youngstown State University, Art Department

Northeastern Ohio Writing Region
Affiliate: Writing Project at Kent State University

Southern Ohio, Northern Kentucky and Southeastern
Indiana Art Region
Affiliate: Art Machine, Inc.

South Dakota
South Dakota Art Region
Affiliate: University of South Dakota

Wisconsin
Wisconsin Art Region
Affiliate: The Milwaukee Art Museum

Milwaukee Writing Region
Affiliate: Still Waters Collective

Southeast Wisconsin Scholastic Writing Region
Affiliate: Harborside Academy

Southwest

Arizona
Arizona Art & Writing Region
Affiliate: Young Authors of Arizona (YAA)

Louisiana
North-Central Louisiana Writing Region
Affiliate: Northwestern State University Writing Project

Southeast Louisiana Writing Region
Affiliate: Greater New Orleans Writing Project

New Mexico
New Mexico Art Region
Affiliate: New Mexico Art Education Association

Oklahoma
Oklahoma Art Region
Affiliate: Tulsa Community College Liberal Arts Department

Texas
Harris County Art & Writing Region
Affiliate: Harris County Department of Education

San Antonio Art Region
Affiliate: SAY Sí (San Antonio Youth Yes)

Travis County Art Region
Affiliate: St. Stephen's School

West Texas Art Region
Affiliate: Wayland Baptist University, Department of Art

ACKNOWLEDGEMENTS

The Alliance for Young Artists & Writers gratefully acknowledges the thousands of educators who encourage students to submit their works to the Scholastic Art & Writing Awards each year and the remarkable students who have the courage to put their art and writing before panels of renowned jurors. We would like to especially recognize the National Writing Project for its far-reaching effects in the writing community and its continued commitment to our program. In addition, our mission is greatly furthered through special partnerships with the National Writing Project, National Art Education Association, the Association of Independent Colleges of Art and Design, and the NAACP's ACT-SO program.

SUPPORT THE SCHOLASTIC ART & WRITING AWARDS

As a nonprofit organization, our ability to recognize and honor creative teens across the country is made possible through the generosity of our supporters. The Alliance for Young Artists & Writers is grateful to our generous sponsors, who provide funds to create and produce all our programs, including the Scholastic Awards, the Art.Write.Now.Tour, the Alliance Summer Arts Program, and more: Scholastic Inc., the Maurice R. Robinson Fund, Command Web Offset Co., The New York Times, Kramer Levin Naftalis & Frankel LLP, the National Endowment for the Arts, Blick Art Materials & Utrecht Art Supplies, the Gedenk Movement, Bloomberg Philanthropies, Golden Artist Colors, the New York City Department of Cultural Affairs, Duck Tape®; numerous other individual, foundation, and corporate funders; and, for the National Student Poets Program, the Institute of Museum and Library Services and the President's Committee on the Arts and the Humanities.

The Best Teen Writing is made possible through the generous support of our donors. *The Best Teen Writing of 2015* is supported by a special gift from The Malkin Fund.

Our donors—hundreds of corporations, foundations, organizations, and individuals alike—make the Scholastic Art & Writing Awards possible year after year. Without them, the Alliance for Young Artists & Writers would not be able to celebrate, recognize, and support the remarkable efforts of creative teens across the country. We are extremely grateful for this support.

Please join us! Your show of financial support means that the arts matter and that writing counts. It means that the work our extraordinary educators do every day in the classroom is invaluable. It means that youth voices are important and deserve to be heard. Most importantly, your support says that the future of a healthy society starts with the kinds of opportunities we provide for our youth.

Contributions in any amount are greatly appreciated, go directly toward supporting programs and scholarships for students and alumni, and are tax deductible.

Help support the Awards today! Your support will go a long way toward making the Awards possible for future generations of creative teens. Visit **www.artandwriting.org/donate** to make a contribution online, or send your gift to Alliance for Young Artists & Writers, 557 Broadway, New York, NY 10012.

Thank you!

Ex Libris

This book was made possible in part by a generous gift from The Malkin Fund

50241166R00180

Made in the USA
San Bernardino, CA
17 June 2017